MW00595987

McDougal Littell

MODERN
WORLD
HISTORY

PATTERNS OF INTERACTION

California Consultant

Neal Cates
Long Beach Unified School District
Lakewood, California

McDougal Littell
A DIVISION OF HOUGHTON MIFFLIN COMPANY

ART CREDITS

xx Versailles Treaty. © 2001, *St. Louis Post-Dispatch*. **86** Hitler and Stalin. *Daily Mail*, London, 23 June 1941. Reprinted with permission.

ACKNOWLEDGMENTS

History-Social Science Content Standards for California Public Schools reproduced by permission, California Department of Education, CDE Press, 1430 N Street, Suite 3207, Sacramento, CA 95814

ISBN-13: 978-0-618-57708-8   ISBN-10: 0-618-57708-4

Printed in the United States of America.

8 9 – CKI – 09 08 07

Contents

v

How to Use This Book

The *California Standards Enrichment Workbook* is yours to mark on, to write in, and to make your own. You can use it in class and take it home. The workbook will help you master social studies curriculum, point by point.

For each specific objective or goal in the Grade 10 California Content Standards, your book contains:

- a **Review** page, to summarize the most important content—the issues, ideas, and people behind important events.

- a **Practice** page, that asks you to recall, interpret, analyze, and apply the historical knowledge.

Complete the pages in the order your teacher assigns them. Your teacher will assign pages that match material in your social studies textbook.

You can use the **Quick Prep** section (pages 1–16) to scan important historic eras, leaders, data, and dates, and to look up and learn key terms. The Quick Prep section serves as a handy reference:

- As you work on Review and Practice pages, you can look up key ideas, dates, and definitions.

- The data can help you make inferences, make connections, or answer your own questions as they arise.

- Before a big test, you might use the Quick Prep to review with a peer, a tutor or family member, or on your own.

California History-Social Science Standards

GRADE 10 History-Social Science Content Standards
Reporting Cluster 1: Development of Modern Political Thought

10.1 **Students relate the moral and ethical principles in ancient Greek and Roman philosophy, in Judaism, and in Christianity to the development of Western political thought.**

1. Analyze the similarities and differences in Judeo-Christian and Greco-Roman views of law, reason and faith, and duties of the individual.

2. Trace the development of the Western political ideas of the rule of law and illegitimacy of tyranny, using selections from Plato's Republic and Aristotle's Politics.

3. Consider the influence of the U.S. Constitution on political systems in the contemporary world.

10.2 **Students compare and contrast the Glorious Revolution of England, the American Revolution, and the French Revolution and their enduring effects worldwide on the political expectations for self-government and individual liberty.**

1. Compare the major ideas of philosophers and their effects on the democratic revolutions in England, the United States, France, and Latin America (e.g., John Locke, Charles-Louis Montesquieu, Jean-Jacques Rousseau, Simón Bolívar, Thomas Jefferson, James Madison).

2. List the principles of the Magna Carta, the English Bill of Rights, (1689), the American Declaration of Independence (1776), the French Declaration of the Rights of Man and the Citizen (1789), and the U.S. Bill of Rights (1791).

3. Understand the unique character of the American Revolution, its spread to other parts of the world and its continuing significance to other nations.

4. Explain how the ideology of the French Revolution led France to develop from constitutional monarchy to democratic despotism to the Napoleonic empire.

5. Discuss how nationalism spread across Europe with Napoleon but was repressed for a generation under the Congress of Vienna and Concert of Europe until the Revolutions of 1848.

10.3 **Students analyze the effects of the Industrial Revolution in England, France, Germany, Japan, and the United States.**

1. Analyze why England was the first country to industrialize.

2. Examine how scientific and technological changes and new forms of energy brought about massive social, economic, and cultural exchange (e.g., the inventions and discoveries of James Watt, Eli Whitney, Henry Bessemer, Louis Pasteur, Thomas Edison).

3. Describe the growth of population, rural to urban migration, and growth of cities associated with the Industrial Revolution.

4. Trace the evolution of work and labor, including the demise of the slave trade and the effects of immigration, mining and manufacturing, division of labor, and the union movement.

5. Understand the connections among natural resources, entrepreneurship, labor, and capital in an industrial economy.

6. Analyze the emergence of capitalism as a dominant economic pattern and the responses to it, including Utopianism, Social Democracy, Socialism, and Communism.

7. Describe the emergence of Romanticism in art and literature (e.g., the poetry of William Blake and William Wordsworth), social criticism (e.g., the novels of Charles Dickens), and the move away from Classicism in Europe.

10.4 **Students analyze patterns of global change in the era of New Imperialism in at least two of the following regions or countries: Africa, Southeast Asia, China, India, Latin America, and the Philippines.**

1. Describe the rise of industrial economies and their link to imperialism and colonialism (e.g., the role played by national security and strategic advantage; moral issues raised by the search for national hegemony, Social Darwinism, and the missionary impulse; material issues such as land, resources, and technology).

2. Discuss the locations of the colonial rule of such nations as England, France, Germany, Italy, Japan, the Netherlands, Russia, Spain, Portugal, and the United States.

3. Explain imperialism from the perspective of the colonizers and the colonized and the varied immediate and long-term responses by the people under colonial rule.

4. Describe the independence struggles of the colonized regions of the world, including the roles of leaders, such as Sun Yat-sen in China, and the roles of ideology and religion.

GRADE 10 History-Social Science Content Standards
Reporting Cluster 3: Causes and Effects of the First World War

10.5   Students analyze the causes and course of the First World War.

1.   Analyze the arguments for entering into war presented by leaders from all sides of the Great War and the role of political and economic rivalries, ethnic and ideological conflicts, domestic discontent and disorder, and propaganda and nationalism in mobilizing the civilian population in support of "total war."

2.   Examine the principal theaters of battle, major turning points, and the importance of geographic factors in military decisions and outcomes (e.g., topography, waterways, distance, climate).

3.   Explain how the Russian Revolution and the entry of the United States affected the course and outcome of the war.

4.   Understand the nature of the war and its human costs (military and civilian) on all sides of the conflict, including how colonial peoples contributed to the war effort.

5.   Discuss human rights violations and genocide, including the Ottoman government's actions against Armenian citizens.

10.6   Students analyze the effects of the First World War.

1.   Analyze the aims and negotiating roles of world leaders, the terms and influence of the Treaty of Versailles and Woodrow Wilson's Fourteen Points, and the causes and effects of the United States's rejection of the League of Nations on world politics.

2.   Describe the effects of the war and resulting peace treaties on population movement, the international economy, and shifts in the geographic and political borders of Europe and the Middle East.

3.   Understand the widespread disillusionment with prewar institutions, authorities, and values that resulted in a void that was later filled by totalitarians.

4.   Discuss the influence of World War I on literature, art, and intellectual life in the West (e.g., Pablo Picasso, the "lost generation" of Gertrude Stein, Ernest Hemingway).

GRADE 10 History-Social Science Content Standards
Reporting Cluster 4: Causes and Effects of the Second World War

10.7 Students analyze the rise of totalitarian governments after World War I.

1. Understand the cause and consequences of the Russian Revolution, including Lenin's use of totalitarianism means to seize and maintain control (e.g., the Gulag).

2. Trace Stalin's rise to power in the Soviet Union and the connection between economic policies, political policies, the absence of a free press, and systematic violations of human rights (e.g., the Terror Famine in Ukraine).

3. Analyze the rise, aggression, and human costs of totalitarian regimes (Fascist and Communist) in Germany, Italy, and the Soviet Union, noting especially their common and dissimilar traits.

10.8 Students analyze the causes and consequences of World War II.

1. Compare the German, Italian, and Japanese drives for empire in the 1930s, including the 1936 Rape of Nanking, other atrocities in China, and the Stalin-Hitler Pact of 1939.

2. Understand the role of appeasement, nonintervention (isolationism), and the domestic distractions in Europe and the United States prior to the outbreak of World War II.

3. Identify and locate the Allied and Axis powers on a map and discuss the major turning points of the war, the principal theaters of conflict, key strategic decisions, and the resulting war conferences and political resolutions, with emphasis on the importance of geographic factors.

4. Describe the political, diplomatic, and military leaders during the war (e.g., Winston Churchill, Franklin Delano Roosevelt, Emperor Hirohito, Adolf Hitler, Benito Mussolini, Joseph Stalin, Douglas MacArthur, Dwight Eisenhower).

5. Analyze the Nazi policy of pursuing racial purity, especially against the European Jews; its transformation into the Final Solution; and the Holocaust that resulted in the murder of six million Jewish civilians.

6. Discuss the human costs of the war, with particular attention to the civilian and military losses in Russia, Germany, Britain, the United States, China, and Japan.

10.9 **Students analyze the international developments in the post–World War II world.**

1. Compare the economic and military power shifts caused by the war, including the Yalta Pact, the development of nuclear weapons, Soviet control over Eastern European nations, and the economic recoveries of Germany and Japan.

2. Analyze the causes of the Cold War, with the free world on one side and Soviet client states on the other, including competition for influence in such places as Egypt, the Congo, Vietnam, and Chile.

3. Understand the importance of the Truman Doctrine and the Marshall Plan, which established the pattern for America's postwar policy of supplying economic and military aid to prevent the spread of Communism and the resulting economic and political competition in arenas such as Southeast Asia (i.e., the Korean War, Vietnam War), Cuba, and Africa.

4. Analyze the Chinese Civil War, the rise of Mao Tse-tung, and the subsequent political and economic upheavals in China (e.g., the Great Leap Forward, the Cultural Revolution, and the Tiananmen Square uprising).

5. Describe the uprisings in Poland (1952), Hungary (1956), and Czechoslovakia (1968) and those countries' resurgence in the 1970s and 1980s as people in Soviet satellites sought freedom from Soviet control.

6. Understand how the forces of nationalism developed in the Middle East, how the Holocaust affected world opinion regarding the need for a Jewish state, and the significance and effects of the location and establishment of Israel on world affairs.

7. Analyze the reasons for the collapse of the Soviet Union, including the weakness of the command economy, burdens of military commitments, and growing resistance to Soviet rule by dissidents in satellite states and the non-Russian Soviet republics.

8. Discuss the establishment and work of the United Nations and the purposes and functions of the Warsaw Pact, SEATO, NATO, and the Organization of American States.

10.10 **Students analyze instances of nation-building in the contemporary world in at least two of the following regions or countries: the Middle East, Africa, Mexico and other parts of Latin America, and China.**

1. Understand the challenges in the regions, including their geopolitical, cultural, military, and economic significance and the international relationships in which they are involved.

2. Describe the recent history of the regions, including political divisions and systems, key leaders, religious issues, natural features, resources, and population patterns.

3. Discuss the important trends in the regions today and whether they appear to serve the cause of individual freedom and democracy.

10.11 **Students analyze the integration of countries into the world economy and the information, technological, and communications revolutions (e.g., television, satellites, computers).**

California History and Social Science Analysis Skills (Grade 10)

Chronological and Spatial Thinking

CST 1 Students compare the present with the past, evaluating the consequences of past events and decisions and determining the lessons that were learned.

CST 2 Students analyze how change happens at different rates at different times; that some aspects can change while other remain the same; and understand that change is complicated and affects not only technology and politics but also values and beliefs.

CST 3 Students use a variety of maps and documents to interpret human movement, including major patterns of domestic and international migration, changing environmental preferences and settlement patterns, the frictions that develop between population groups, and the diffusion of ideas, technological innovations, and goods.

CST 4 Students relate current events to the physical and human characteristics of places and regions.

Historical Research, Evidence, and Point of View

REP 1 Students distinguish valid arguments from fallacious arguments in historical interpretations.

REP 2 Students identify bias and prejudice in historical interpretations.

REP 3 Students evaluate major debates among historians concerning alternative interpretations of the past, including an analysis of authors' use of evidence and the distinctions between sound generalizations and misleading oversimplifications.

REP 4 Students construct and test hypotheses; collect, evaluate, and employ information from multiple primary and secondary sources; and apply it in oral and written presentations.

Historical Interpretation

HI 1 Students show the connections, casual and otherwise, between particular historical events and larger social, economic, and political trends and developments.

HI 2 Students recognize the complexity of historical causes and effects, including the limitations of determining cause and effect.

HI 3 Students interpret past events and issues within the context in which an event unfolded rather than solely in terms of present day norms and values.

HI 4 Students understand the meaning, implication, and impact of historical events while recognizing that events could have taken other directions.

HI 5 Students analyze human modifications of a landscape and examine the resulting environmental policy issues.

HI 6 Students conduct cost/benefit analyses and apply basic economic indicators to analyze the aggregate economic behavior of the U.S. economy.

Major Events in World History

This Quick Prep section provides a handy reference to key facts on a variety of topics in world history.

Time and Place	Event	Significance
40,000 B.C. Europe	Cro-Magnons appear.	Ancestors of modern humans
8000 B.C. Africa, Asia	Agriculture begins.	One of the great breakthroughs in human history, setting the stage for the development of civilizations
3100 B.C. Egypt	Upper and Lower Egypt unite.	The Kingdom of Egypt, ruled by pharaohs, began a 3,000-year period of unity and cultural continuity.
3000 B.C. Mesopotamia	Civilization emerges in Sumer.	One of the world's first civilizations
2500 B.C. Indus Valley	Planned cities arise.	Beginning of the Indus Valley civilization; many features of modern Indian culture can be traced to this early civilization.
2350 B.C. Mesopotamia	Sargon of Akkad builds an empire.	World's first empire, which extended from the Mediterranean coast in the west to present-day Iran in the east
2000 B.C. China	Xia Dynasty emerges.	This was the first Chinese dynasty. Along the Huang He, farming settlements grew into cities.
1700 B.C. Asian steppes	Indo-Europeans begin migrations.	The Indo-Europeans moved into Europe, the Middle East, and India, spreading their languages and changing cultures.
1532 B.C. China	Shang Dynasty begins.	The first Chinese civilization, which arose along the Huang He
1200 B.C. Mexico	Olmec culture arises.	Oldest known civilization in the Americas
850 B.C. Assyria	Assyria builds an empire.	Using military force to conquer and rule, the Assyrians established an empire that included most of the old centers of power in Southwest Asia and Egypt.
800 B.C. Greece	Greek city-states arise.	Led to the development of several political systems, including democracy
550 B.C. Persia	Cyrus builds the Persian Empire.	Characterized by tolerance and wise government
500 B.C. Rome	Romans establish a republic.	Source of some of the most fundamental values and institutions of Western civilization
461 B.C. Greece	Age of Pericles begins.	Democratic principles and classical Greek culture flourished, leaving a legacy that endures to the present day.
334 B.C. Greece	Alexander begins to build an empire.	Conquered Persia and Egypt; extended his empire to the Indus River in India; resulted in a blending of Greek, Egyptian, and Eastern customs
321 B.C. India	Mauryan Empire is established.	United north India politically for the first time
202 B.C. China	Han Dynasty replaces Qin dynasty.	Expanded China's borders; developed a system of government that lasted for centuries
27 B.C. Rome	Octavian rules Roman Empire.	Took the title of Augustus and ruled the mightiest empire of the ancient world; began the Pax Romana, a 200-year period of peace and prosperity; Roman way of life spread throughout the empire.
A.D. 29 Jerusalem	Jesus is crucified.	Christianity spread throughout the Roman Empire.
A.D. 100 South America	Moche civilization emerges.	Built an advanced society in Peru
A.D. 100s Africa	Bantu migrations begin.	Bantu speakers spread their language and culture throughout southern Africa.
A.D. 320 India	Gupta Empire begins.	A great flowering of Indian civilization, especially Hindu culture

Time and Place	Event	Significance
527 Constantinople	Justinian I becomes Byzantine emperor.	Recovered and ruled almost all the former territory of the Roman Empire; created a body of civil laws called Justinian's Code; built beautiful churches
600 Central America	Maya civilization thrives.	Built spectacular cities and developed the most advanced writing system in the ancient Americas
618 China	Tang dynasty begins.	Created a powerful empire, improved trade and agriculture, and restored the civil service bureaucracy
622 Arabia	Muhammad leaves Mecca.	The hegira (emigration) of Muhammad marked the founding of Islam, now the world's second-largest faith.
800 North America	Anasazi civilization develops.	Ancestors of the Pueblo peoples
800s–900s West Africa	Empire of Ghana thrives.	Built its wealth on the trans-Saharan gold-salt trade
814 Western Europe	Charlemagne unites much of Europe.	Established the Carolingian Empire
960 China	Sung Dynasty begins.	China became the most populous and advanced country in the world.
1095 France	Pope Urban II issues call for First Crusade.	Stimulated trade, weakened the power of the pope and feudal nobles, and left a legacy of distrust between Christians and Muslims
1192 Japan	Kamakura Shogunate begins.	First shogunate, which set the pattern for military dictators, called shoguns, to rule Japan until 1868
1200s Mexico	Aztec civilization begins.	Built the greatest empire in Mesoamerica
1200s Peru	Inca Empire begins.	The largest empire in the Americas
1209 Mongolia	Genghis Khan begins Mongol conquests.	Built the largest unified land empire in world history
1215 England	King John agrees to Magna Carta.	The Magna Carta contributed to modern concepts of jury trials and legal rights.
1235 Africa	Sundiata founds Mali Empire.	Became a powerful center of commerce and trade in West Africa
1279 China	Kublai Khan conquers Sung Dynasty.	Completed the conquest of China and encouraged trade; Chinese ideas then began to influence Western civilization.
1300 Italy	Renaissance begins.	Revival of classical studies, revolutionized art, literature, and society
1337 France	Hundred Years' War begins.	Ended the Middle Ages
1347 Italy	Bubonic plague spreads to Europe.	Killed nearly one-third of Europe's population and disrupted medieval society
1368 China	Ming Dynasty begins.	Ended Mongol rule of China and made China the dominant power in the region
1453 Turkey	Constantinople falls to Turks.	One of the most influential cities of the 15th century, Constantinople became part of the Ottoman Empire, and its name was changed to Istanbul.
1492 Americas	Columbus sails to Hispaniola.	Opened the way for European settlement of the Americas
1517 Germany	Martin Luther begins Reformation.	Led to the founding of Protestant churches
1526 India	Babur founds Mughal Empire.	Brought Turks, Persians, and Indians together in a vast empire
1529 Anatolia	Suleiman the Magnificent rules Ottoman Empire.	The Ottoman Empire reached its greatest size and grandeur.
1603 Japan	Tokugawa Shogunate begins.	Unified Japan and began a 200-year period of isolation and prosperity
1607 North America	English settle at Jamestown.	England's first permanent settlement in North America

Time and Place	Event	Significance
1644 China	Manchus found Qing dynasty.	The Manchus ruled China for 260 years and brought Taiwan, Chinese Central Asia, Mongolia, and Tibet into China.
1700s Europe	Enlightenment thought develops.	Philosophers promoted ideas about representative government and individual rights that helped to spur democratic revolutions.
1775 North America	American Revolution breaks out.	American revolutionaries threw off British rule and established a successful republic—the United States.
1789 France	French Revolution begins.	The French Revolution ended the Old Regime and brought on the Reign of Terror.
1805–1812 France	Napoleon conquers most of Europe.	Built the largest European empire since the Roman Empire
1821 Mexico	Mexico declares independence.	Mexico and many other Latin American countries fought colonial rule and gained their independence about this time.
1848 Europe	Revolutions sweep Europe.	A system of nation-states became established in Europe.
1854 Japan	Treaty of Kanagawa gives U.S. access to two ports.	Japan ended its isolation from the rest of the world.
1865 United States	Civil War ends.	The United States remained one nation and slavery ended.
1871 Germany	Franco-Prussian War ends.	The final stage in the unification of Germany
1884–1885 Germany	Berlin Conference takes place.	European powers divided among them almost the entire continent of Africa, which remained largely colonized until the 1960s.
1911 China	Qing dynasty is overthrown.	Ended thousands of years of imperial rule and made China a republic under Sun Yat-sen.
1914 Europe	World War I begins.	Became the largest war the world had ever seen
1917 Russia	Russian Revolution occurs.	Ended the rule of the czars and ushered in the first communist government
1939 Europe	Germany invades Poland.	The beginning of World War II, which caused more death and destruction than any other conflict in history
1945 Japan	United States drops atomic bombs.	Japan surrendered, and World War II ended.
1945 United States	United Nations charter is signed.	With 191 member nations, the UN is now the world's leading peacekeeping organization.
1949 China	Chinese Communists take over China.	China split into two nations, one on the island of Taiwan and one on the mainland. On the mainland, Communist China expanded its territory and reshaped its economy based on Marxist socialism.
1957 Vietnam	Vietnam War begins.	The war continued until 1975, deeply divided Americans, and ended with North Vietnamese Communists taking over South Vietnam.
1990 Germany	Berlin Wall falls.	Germany became unified again.
1991 Soviet Union	Soviet Union breaks up.	The Cold War ended.
2001 United States	September 11 Terrorist Attacks	Terrorists attacked the United States, crashing planes into strategic targets, killing thousands of civilians.

Major Eras in World History

The term *era*, or *age*, refers to a broad period of time characterized by a shared pattern of life. Eras and ages typically do not have exact starting and ending points. Because the historical development of different regions of the world is varied, no single listing of eras applies to all of world history. This chart applies primarily to Western civilization.

Era and Dates	Description
Stone Age (2.5 million–3000 B.C.)	This long prehistoric period is often divided into two parts: the Old Stone Age, or Paleolithic Age, and the New Stone Age, or Neolithic Age. The Paleolithic Age lasted from about 2.5 million to 8000 B.C. During this time, hominids made and used stone tools and learned to control fire. The Neolithic Age began about 8000 B.C.) and ended about 3000 B.C.) in some areas. In this period, people learned to polish stone tools, make pottery, grow crops, and raise animals. The introduction of agriculture, a major turning point in human history, is called the Neolithic Revolution.
Bronze Age (3000–1200 B.C.)	People began using bronze, rather than stone and copper, to make tools and weapons. The Bronze Age began in Sumer about 3000 B.C.) when Sumerian metalworkers found that they could melt together certain amounts of copper and tin to make bronze. The first civilizations emerged during the Bronze Age.
Iron Age (1500–1000 B.C. to the present day)	The use of iron to make tools and weapons became widespread. The Iron Age is the last technological stage in the Stone-Bronze-Iron ages sequence.
Classical Greece (2000 B.C.–300 B.C.)	Greek culture developed, rose to new heights, and spread to other lands. The Greek city-states established the first democratic governments. Greek scientists made advances in mathematics, medicine, and other fields. The Greeks produced great works of drama, poetry, sculpture, architecture, and philosophy that still influence people today.
Roman Empire (500 B.C.–A.D. 500)	At its height, the Roman Empire united much of Europe, the north coast of Africa, and a large part of the Middle East. The Romans admired Greek art, literature, architecture, and science, and so they adopted and preserved much of Greek culture. The Romans also created their own legacy with outstanding achievements in engineering, architecture, the arts, and law. The Romans spread Christianity throughout Europe, and their official language—Latin—gave rise to French, Italian, Spanish, and other Romance languages. Western civilization has its roots in Greco-Roman culture.
Middle Ages (500–1200)	The West Roman Empire fell to Germanic conquerors who formed kingdoms out of former Roman provinces. A new political and military system called feudalism became established. Nobles were granted the use of lands that belonged to their king in exchange for their loyalty, military service, and protection of the peasants who worked the land. Western Europe became divided into feudal states. The Middle Ages was the time of castles and knights.
Renaissance and Reformation (1300–1600)	The Renaissance was a period of rebirth of learning and the arts based on a revival of classical study. The study of Greek classics gave rise to an intellectual movement called humanism, which emphasized human potential and achievements rather than religious concerns. The works of the Italian artists Leonardo da Vinci and Michelangelo and the English dramatist William Shakespeare represent the cultural height of the Renaissance. The Reformation was a movement for religious reform that led to the founding of Protestant churches. These churches rejected the authority of the pope, and the power of the Roman Catholic Church declined.
Exploration and Colonization 1400–1800	The monarchs of Europe financed voyages around the world, motivated by the desire for riches and the hope of spreading Christianity. Seeking spices and converts, European explorers made long sea journeys to the East. Searching for a shorter sea route to Asia, Christopher Columbus landed in the Caribbean islands and opened up the New World to European colonization. The establishment of colonies and trading networks led to a great worldwide cultural exchange, the devastation of Native American cultures in the New World, and the enslavement of millions of Africans.
Revolution and Independence 1700–1900	Movements toward democracy and nationalism affected most countries in the Western world. These movements sparked the Revolutionary War in America, which resulted in the independence of the British colonies and the birth of the United States. They also sparked the ten-year French Revolution. Many Latin American nations fought colonial rule and gained their independence. In Europe, great empires fell and a system of nation-states became established.

Era and Dates	Description
Industrial Revolution 1700–1900	The spread of power-driven machines sparked the rapid growth of industry in Great Britain, the United States, and continental Europe. People began working in large factories, rather than homes and small workshops, to produce goods. Industrialization made possible a great increase in the production of manufactured goods. A worldwide system of markets developed as industrial nations imported raw materials and exported manufactured goods. Industrialization dramatically transformed people's lives. People moved from rural areas to cities, and the middle class increased in size. European nations divided up most of Africa, acquiring colonies to feed their factories with raw materials.
Warring World 1900–1945	The first half of the 1900s was marked by warfare on a larger scale than ever before. Rivalries among European powers led to a system of military alliances that drew Europe and other regions into World War I (1914–1918). The Allies, which included France, Britain, Russia, Italy, and the United States, defeated the Central Powers, which included Germany, Austria-Hungary, and the Ottoman Empire. The victorious Allies dictated harsh peace terms that left hard feelings and set the stage for World War II. World War I also helped ignite the Russian Revolutions of 1917, which replaced czarist rule with the world's first communist government. The expansionism of Germany and Japan led to World War II (1939–1945). Germany, Japan, Italy, and other Axis powers were defeated by Britain, the Soviet Union, the United States, and the other Allies. The war cost millions of lives and left Europe and Japan economically and socially devastated.
Cold War 1946–1991	After World War II, countries with two conflicting economic systems—capitalism and communism—competed for worldwide influence and power. The major players in this struggle, the United States and the Soviet Union, each tried to win other nations to its side. They used military, economic, and humanitarian aid to extend their control over other countries. Each sought to prevent the other superpower from gaining influence. The rivalry was mainly diplomatic and strategic and hence was called the Cold War. However, it led both the United States and the Soviet Union to become involved in military actions around the world. The rivalry dominated world politics for four decades, until the Soviet Union broke up in 1991.

Major Religions

	Buddhism	Christianity	Hinduism	Islam	Judaism	Confucianism
Followers worldwide (estimated 2003 figures)	364 million	2 billion	828 million	1.2 billion	14.5 million	6.3 million
Name of god	no god	God	Brahman	Allah	God	no god
Founder	the Buddha	Jesus	no founder	no founder but spread by Muhammad	Abraham	Confucius
Holy book	many sacred books, including the Dhammapada	Bible, including Old Testament and New Testament	many sacred texts, including the Upanishads	Qur'an	Hebrew Bible, including the Torah	*Analects*
Clergy	Buddhist monks	priests, ministers, monks, and nuns	Brahmin priests, monks, and gurus	no clergy but a scholar class, called the ulama, and imams, who may lead prayers	rabbis	no clergy
Basic beliefs	• Followers can achieve enlightenment by understanding The Four Noble Truths and by following The Noble Eightfold Path of right opinions, right desires, right speech, right action, right job, right effort, right concentration, and right meditation.	• There is only one God, who watches over and cares for his people. • Jesus is the Son of God. He died to save humanity. His death and resurrection made eternal life possible for others.	• The soul never dies but is continually reborn until it becomes divinely enlightened. • Persons achieve happiness and divine enlightenment after they free themselves from their earthly desires. • Freedom from earthly desires comes from many lifetimes of worship, knowledge, and virtuous acts.	• Persons achieve salvation by following the Five Pillars of Islam and living a just life. The pillars are faith, prayer, charity, fasting, and pilgrimage to Mecca.	• There is only one God, who watches over and cares for his people. • God loves and protects his people but also holds people accountable for their sins and shortcomings. • Persons serve God by studying the Torah and living by its teachings.	• Social order, harmony, and good government should be based on strong family relationships. • Respect for parents and elders is important to a well-ordered society. • Education is important for the welfare of both the individual and society.

Source: *World Almanac 2004*

Major Inventions of the Modern Age

Some dates are historically debated.

Invention	Date	Significance
Magnifying Glass	1250	Used for study of small matter and used in crafts
Gun / Cannon	1260	Enabled weapons to be used at long range for better defense
Mechanical Clock	1360	Allowed better planning, especially in cities and in traveling
Printing Press	1454	Spread written information and scholarship and new ideas, especially in religion
Cast Iron Pipe	1455	A conduit for water and sewage; improved sanitation
Graphite Pencil	1560	Helped in art, science, mathematics and education for drafting ideas
Microscope	1590	Allowed study of cells and microorganisms; new knowledge of life processes
Telescope	1608	Study of the stars, planets, objects, and motion in space; better navigation
Submarine	1620	Used for ocean exploration and later for warfare
Analytic Geometry	1637	System for describing points, planes, and curves in abstract space
Steam Engine	1639	Helped pave the way for the industrial revolution
Barometer	1643	Measured atmospheric pressure; allowed more accurate weather prediction
Tourniquet	1674	Used in medicine to apply pressure and stop blood flow to a part of the body
Piano	1709	Produced a greater range of sounds than previous musical instruments
Mercury Thermometer	1714	Measured heat by degrees; improved chemistry, meteorology, and medicine
Ship Chronometer	1728	Allowed timekeeping at sea; led to longitude measurements; improved mapping
Threshing Machine	1732	Sped up crop production; improved farming
Classification of Species	1735	Allowed shared data about global discoveries within a scientific naming system
Wool Carding Machine	1743	Sped production of fibers for wool cloth
Leyden Jar	1746	First electrical condensor, led to understanding of current and circuits
Dynamometer	1750	Measured mechanical forces, used in developing new machines
Watt's Steam Engine	1769	More efficient engine powered the industrial revolution
Cotton Gin	1793	Cotton could be cleaned by machine rather than by hand; sped production
Smallpox Vaccine	1796	helped stop the spread of epidemic disease
Locomotive	1825	First locomotive and first passenger railroad, sped shipping and transport
Photograph	1826	Faithful production of images from life by machine
Telegraph	1837	First long-distance communication without human travel
Bessemer Steelmaking	1850s	Furnace hot enough to melt iron and carbon; facilitated steel and skyscrapers
Pasteurization	1860s	Sterilization of liquids; increased shelf-life of milk and other perishables
Telephone	1876	Person-to-person long-distance communication by speech
Edison's Light Bulb	1879	Made long-lasting indoor electric lighting possible
Automobile	1885–96	First gas engine, diesel engine, motorcycle, automobile, and tires
Radioactivity (X-Ray)	1895–8	Accidental X-ray led to discovery of radioactivity; used in medicine and energy
Airplane	1903	Sped transportation and shipping, also maximized military weapons
Television	1923	Long-distance transmission and receipt of sound and moving image
Rocket	1926	First liquid-propelled rocket, led to later space flight
Penicillin	1928	mold spores that killed bacteria, later used to cure bacterial infections, led to other antibiotics
Satellite	1957	Mechanical explorer able to orbit Earth through space; used for communications, surveillance, weapons, and space exploration
Computer	1964	Used for engineering; data storage, sharing, and processing; robotics and other artificial intelligence applications
Global Computer Network	1969	U.S. Defense Department creates ARPANET; precursor to 1991 Internet
Genetic Engineering	1973	First successful recombination of DNA; led to improved food production

Major World Documents

Time and Place	Event	Significance
Analects (about 400 B.C.)	Followers of Confucius	Teachings of Confucius
Bill of Rights (adopted 1791)	Members of Congress	First 10 amendments to the U.S. Constitution, outlining the rights and liberties of American citizens
Code of Hammurabi (1700s B.C.)	Hammurabi	Collection of laws for Babylonian Empire
Dead Sea Scrolls (about 200 B.C.–A.D. 70)	Probably the Essenes, a Jewish sect	Ancient manuscripts from Palestine that include the oldest manuscript of the Hebrew Bible
Declaration of Independence (1776)	Thomas Jefferson	Statement of the American colonists' reasons for declaring independence from Great Britain
Declaration of the Rights of Man (1789)	French National Assembly	Statement of the rights of French men
English Bill of Rights (1689)	English Parliament	List of the rights of Englishmen
Hebrew Bible (after 1000 B.C.)	Unknown	Sacred book of Judaism
Justinian Code (A.D. 528–533)	Panel of legal experts appointed by Byzantine emperor Justinian	Collection of early Roman laws and legal opinions
Magna Carta (1215)	English nobles	Guaranteed rights of English nobles
Mayflower Compact (1620)	Pilgrim leaders	First written agreement for self-government in America
New Testament (after about A.D. 70)	Unknown	Sacred book of Christianity
Ninty-Five Theses (1517)	Martin Luther	Statements addressing problems within the Catholic Church
Popol Vuh (1500s)	Unknown	Creation story of the Maya
Qur'an (A.D. 610–632)	Considered to be revelations from the angel Gabriel to Muhammad	Sacred book of Muslims
The Republic (375 B.C.?)	Plato	Description of ideal state of society
Two Treatises of Government (1690)	John Locke	Ideas on government and natural rights
U.S. Constitution (adopted 1788)	Members of Constitutional Convention	Statement of the form of the United States government
Vedas (about 1400 B.C.)	Unknown	Sacred books of Hinduism

Major Explorations

Area Explored	Dates	Explorer(s)	Nationality
Newfoundland	about 1000	Leif Ericson	Norse
China, Southeast Asia, India	1270s–1290s	Marco Polo	Venetian
West Indies, South and Central America	1492–1502	Christopher Columbus	Italian
Newfoundland	1497	John and Sebastian Cabot	Italian
Cape of Good Hope, Africa; India	1497–1498	Vasco da Gama	Portuguese
East and north coast of South America	1497–1499	Vespucci	Italian
Brazil	1500	Pedro Alvarez Cabral	Portuguese
Panama, Pacific Ocean	1513	Vasco Nunez de Balboa	Spanish
Florida, Yucatán Peninsula	1513	Juan Ponce de Leon	Spanish
Mexico	1519	Hernando Cortés	Spanish
Straits of Magellan, Tierra del Fuego	1519–1520	Ferdinand Magellan	Portuguese
New York harbor	1524	Giovanni da Verrazano	Italian
Texas	1528	Cabeza de Vaca	Spanish
Peru	1532	Francisco Pizarro	Spanish
Canada, Gulf of St. Lawrence	1534	Jacques Cartier	French
Buenos Aires	1536	Pedro de Mendoza	Spanish
Mississippi River, near Memphis	1539–1541	Hernando de Soto	Spanish
Southwestern United States	1540	Francisco de Coronado	Spanish
Colorado River	1540	Hernando Alarcon	Spanish
Colorado, Grand Canyon	1540	Garcia de Lopez Cardenas	Spanish
Amazon River	1541	Francisco de Orellana	Spanish
Western Mexico, San Diego harbor	1542	Juan Rodriguez Cabrillo	Portuguese
California coast	1577–1580	Sir Francis Drake	English
Orinoco river	1595	Sir Walter Raleigh	English
Canadian interior, Lake Champlain	1603–1609	Samuel de Champlain	French
Hudson River, Hudson Bay	1609–1610	Henry Hudson	English
Tasmania	1642	Abel Janszoon	Dutch
Mississippi River, south to Arkansas	1673	Jacques Marquette, Louis Joliet	French
Mississippi River, south to Gulf of Mexico	1682	Robert Cavelier, sieur de La Salle	French
Bering Strait and Alaska	1727–1729	Vitus Bering	Danish
South Pacific	1768–1775	James Cook	English
Northwestern Canada	1789	Sir Alexander Mackenzie	Canadian
Missouri River, Rocky Mountains, Columbia River	1804–1805	Meriwether Lewis, William Clark	American
Arabia, East Africa, Lake Tanganyika	1853–1858	Sir Richard Burton	English
Upper course of Zambezi River, Victoria Falls, Lake Ngami	1849–1873	David Livingstone	Scottish
Congo River	1874–1889	Sir Henry Stanley	Welsh
North Pole	1909	Robert E. Peary, Matthew Henson	American
South Pole	1911	Roald Amundsen	Norwegian
Moon	1969	Neil Armstrong, Edwin Aldrin	American
Mars	1975–2005	Space probes Viking 1 and 2; Mars Rover robots Spirit and Opportunity	American

Major Figures in World History

Name	Who the Person Was	What the Person Did
Abraham (2000 B.C.?)	Hebrew leader	Founded Judaism.
Alexander the Great (356–323 B.C.)	Macedonian king	Built an empire that included Greece, Persia, Egypt, and part of Central Asia.
Aristotle (384–322 B.C.)	Greek philosopher	Summarized most knowledge up to his time and invented rules of logic that contributed to the modern scientific method.
Bonaparte, Napoleon (1769–1821)	French general and emperor	Built a vast French empire and is considered one of the world's great military geniuses along with Alexander the Great, Hannibal, and Julius Caesar.
Caesar, Julius (100–44 B.C.)	Roman general and dictator	Expanded the Roman Empire.
Gandhi, Mohandas K. (1869–1948)	Indian political and religious leader	Helped India gain its independence from Great Britain by a method of nonviolent resistance.
Hitler, Adolf (1889–1945)	German dictator	Initiated World War II and the Holocaust.
Jefferson, Thomas (1743–1826)	American president, architect, and inventor	Wrote the Declaration of Independence.
Jesus (4 B.C.?–A.D. 28?)	Jewish religious leader	Founded Christianity.
King, Martin Luther, Jr. (1929–1968)	American civil rights leader	Led the civil rights movement in the United States during the 1950s and 1960s.
Lenin, Vladimir (1870–1924)	Russian dictator	Founded the Communist Party in Russia and established the world's first Communist Party dictatorship.
Lincoln, Abraham (1809–1865)	American president	Led the United States through the American Civil War.
Locke, John (1632–1704)	English philosopher	Was a leader of the Enlightenment and promoted democratic thinking.
Luther, Martin (1483–1546)	German theologian	Started the Reformation.
Mandela, Nelson (1918–)	South African anti-apartheid leader	Became the first black president of South Africa.
Mao Tse-tung (1893–1976)	Chinese dictator	Led the Communist revolution in China.
Marx, Karl (1818–1883)	German philosopher	Founded the mass movements of democratic socialism and revolutionary communism.
Moses (1300s B.C.?)	Israelite leader	Led the Jews out of Egypt and received the Ten Commandments.
Muhammad (A.D. 570?–632)	Muslim prophet	Founded Islam.
Pericles (494?–429 B.C.)	Greek statesman	Led Athens during its golden age, often called the Age of Pericles.
Plato (427–347 B.C.)	Greek philosopher	Wrote *The Republic,* in which he described his ideal society.
Socrates (469–399 B.C.)	Greek philosopher	Taught students to examine their beliefs and developed a question-and-answer method of teaching called the Socratic method.
Stalin, Joseph (1879–1953)	Soviet dictator	Used terror to transform the Soviet Union into a totalitarian state and to modernize its economy.
Sun Yat-sen (1866–1925)	Chinese leader	Became known as the "father of modern China" for leading a revolution that overthrew the last Chinese emperor.
Washington, George (1732–1799)	American general and president	Commanded the Continental Army during the American Revolution and served as the first president of the United States.

Major Geographic Features

United States and Canada

Climate		Vegetation		Land Forms and Bodies of Water	
Arctic	Semi-arid	Tundra	Mediterranean	Great Lakes	Rocky Mountains
Sub-arctic	Sub-tropical	Coniferous forest	scrub	Gulf of Mexico	Mississippi River
Temperate	Tropical	Broadleaf forest	Semi-desert	Appalachian	
Arid		Grassland	Desert	Mountains	

Latin America

Climate		Vegetation		Land Forms and Bodies of Water	
Tropical	Temperate	Savannah	Tropical rainforest	Orinoco River	Sierra Madre
Sub-tropical	Arid	Semi-desert	Monsoon forest	Andes Mountains	Amazon River
Desert	Semi-arid	Desert	Broadleaf forest		
		Dry tropical scrub			

Europe, Russia, and the Independent Republics

Climate		Vegetation		Land Forms and Bodies of Water	
Sub-arctic	Temperate	Tundra	Grassland	Baltic Sea	Volga River
Steppe	Mediterranean	Coniferous forest	Mediterranean	Mediterranean Sea	Alps Mountains
Tundra	Alpine	Broadleaf forest	scrub	North Sea	Pyrenees
Humid continental				Lake Baikal	Mountains
				Danube River	Ural Mountains
				Rhine River	

North Africa and Southwest Asia

Climate		Vegetation		Land Forms and Bodies of Water	
Desert	Temperate	Semi-desert	Monsoon forest	Red Sea	Sahara Desert
Sub-tropical	Arid	Desert	Dry tropical scrub	Persian Gulf	Nile River
Tropical	Semi-arid			Black Sea	Tigris River
Tropical monsoon				Dead Sea	Euphrates River

Africa South of the Sahara

Climate		Vegetation		Land Forms and Bodies of Water	
Tropical	Semi-arid	Savannah	Dry tropical scrub	Mount Kilimanjaro	Congo River
Sub-tropical	Desert	Semi-desert	Tropical rainforest	Kalahari Desert	Niger River
Arid		Desert	Monsoon forest	Victoria Falls	Zambezi River
				Nile River	

Southern Asia

Climate		Vegetation		Land Forms and Bodies of Water	
Tropical	Sub-tropical	Monsoon forest	Sub-tropical forest	Himalayan	Mekong River
Monsoon	Moderate	Tropical rainforest		Mountains	Arabian Sea
				Mount Everest	South China Sea
				Indus River	Bay of Bengal
				Ganges River	Malay Archipelago

East Asia, Australia, and the Pacific Islands

Climate		Vegetation		Land Forms and Bodies of Water	
Temperate	Sub-tropical	Savannah	Dry tropical scrub	Mount Fuji	Huang He
Arid	Tropical	Semi-desert	Tropical rainforest	Southern Alps	(Yellow River)
Semi-arid		Desert	Monsoon forest	Gobi Desert	Chang Jiang
				Great Barrier Reef	(Yangtze River)

Government and Economic Systems

System	Definition	Example
Government Systems		
aristocracy	Power is in the hands of a hereditary ruling class or nobility. Aristocracy is a form of oligarchy.	Medieval Europe
autocracy	A single person rules with unlimited power. Autocracy is also called dictatorship and despotism.	Pharoahs of ancient Egypt
democracy	Citizens hold political power either directly or through representatives. In a direct democracy, citizens directly make political decisions. In a representative democracy, the citizens rule through elected representatives.	direct democracy: ancient Athens representative democracy: United States since the 1700s
federal	Powers are divided among the federal, or national, government and a number of state governments.	United States since the 1700s
feudalism	A king allows nobles to use his land in exchange for their loyalty, military service, and protection of the people who live on the land.	Medieval Europe
military state	Military leaders rule, supported by the power of the armed forces.	Assyrian Empire
monarchy	A ruling family headed by a king or queen holds political power and may or may not share the power with citizen bodies. In an absolute monarchy, the ruling family has all the power. In a limited or constitutional monarchy, the ruler's power is limited by the constitution or laws of the nation.	absolute monarchy: reign of King Louis XIV of France constitutional monarchy: United Kingdom
oligarchy	A few persons or a small group rule.	most ancient Greek city-states
parliamentary	Legislative and executive functions are combined in a legislature called a parliament.	United Kingdom since the 1200s
presidential	The chief officer is a president who is elected independently of the legislature.	United States since the 1700s
republic	Citizens elect representatives to rule on their behalf.	Roman Republic
theocracy	Religious leaders control the government, relying on religious law and consultation with religious scholars. In early theocracies, the ruler was considered divine.	Aztec Empire
totalitarianism	The government controls every aspect of public and private life and all opposition is suppressed.	Soviet Union under Joseph Stalin

System	Definition	Example
Economic Systems		
command	The production of goods and services is determined by a central government, which usually owns the means of production. Also called a planned economy.	former Soviet Union
communism	All means of production—land, mines, factories, railroads, and businesses—are owned by the people, private property does not exist, and all goods and services are shared equally.	former Soviet Union
free enterprise	Businesses are privately owned and operate competitively for profit, with minimal government interference. Also called capitalism.	United States
manorialism	A lord gives serfs land, shelter, and protection in exchange for work, and almost everything needed for daily life is produced on the manor, or lord's estate.	Medieval Europe
market	The production of goods and services is determined by the demand from consumers. Also called a demand economy.	United States
mixed	A combination of command and market economies is designed to provide goods and services so that all people will benefit.	present-day Israel
socialism	The means of production are owned by the public and operate for the welfare of all.	In many present-day countries, including Denmark and Sweden, the government owns some industries and operates them for the public good.
traditional	Goods and services are exchanged without the use of money. Also called barter.	many ancient civilizations and tribal societies

Key Terms and Names

TERMS

absolute chronology the arrangement of events by specific dates.

anthropologist a scientist who studies the origin and the physical and cultural development of human beings.

archaeologist a scientist who studies the remains of past cultures.

artifact a human-made object, such as a tool, weapon, or piece of jewelry.

capitalism an economic system based on private ownership and on the investment of money in business ventures in order to make a profit.

communism an economic system in which all means of production—land, mines, factories, railroads, and businesses—are owned by the people, private property does not exist, and all goods and services are shared equally.

constitutional republic a republic established by a constitution, or set of basic laws.

constitutional system of government a system of government that operates according to a set of basic laws.

constitutionalism a constitutional system of government.

democracy a government controlled by its citizens, either directly or through representatives.

democratic-republican government a government that gets its power from citizens who elect representatives.

Eastern civilization civilization that has its origins in ancient East Asian civilizations.

Enlightenment an 18th-century European movement in which thinkers attempted to apply the principles of reason and the scientific method to all aspects of society.

era broad time period characterized by a shared pattern of life.

Fascism a political movement that promotes an extreme form of nationalism, a denial of individual rights, and a dictatorial one-party rule.

feudalism a political system in which nobles are granted the use of lands that legally belong to their king, in exchange for their loyalty, military service, and protection of the people who live on the land.

frames of reference a set of ideas that are necessary for interpreting or understanding events or other ideas.

genocide the systematic killing of an entire people.

geographic distribution the geographic occurrence or range of a feature, such as the location of cities.

geographic pattern the geographic configuration of a feature, such as the grouping of cities along a coast.

Greco-Roman relating to ancient Greece and Rome.

historical context the past circumstances in which an event occurred.

historical inquiry close examination of sources in a search for accurate information about past events.

Holocaust a mass slaughter of Jews and other civilians, carried out by the Nazi government of Germany before and during World War II.

imperialism a policy in which a strong nation seeks to dominate other countries politically, economically, or socially.

individualism belief in the importance and value of the individual, or the doctrine that the interests of the individual have priority over those of the state.

Indus river valley area along the Indus River in what is now Pakistan, where one of the world's first civilizations arose about 2500 B.C.

industrialization the development of industries for the machine production of goods.

Judeo-Christian having historical roots in Judaism and Christianity.

Judeo-Christian ethics a set of moral principles or values that has its roots in both Judaism and Christianity.

manorialism economic system in medieval Europe in which a lord gives serfs land, shelter, and protection in exchange for work, and almost everything needed for daily life is produced on the manor, or lord's estate.

Mesoamerica an area extending from central Mexico to Honduras, where several of the ancient civilizations of the Americas developed.

Nazism the fascist policies of the National Socialist German Workers' party, based on totalitarianism, a belief in racial superiority, and state control of industry.

Neolithic agricultural revolution the major change in human life caused by the beginnings of farming—that is, by people's shift from food gathering to food producing.

Nile river valley area in Egypt along the Nile River where one of the world's first civilizations arose between about 3000 and 2000 B.C.

oppression unjust or cruel exercise of power.

parliamentary system of government system in which legislative and executive functions are combined in a legislature called a parliament.

primary source material produced during the period being studied.

relative chronology the arrangement of events in relation to other events.

republicanism belief in a system of government in which political power rests with citizens who vote for representatives responsible to them.

scientific revolution a major change in European thought, starting in the mid-1500s, in which the study of the natural world began to be characterized by careful observation and the questioning of accepted beliefs.

secondary source material prepared after the period being studied by a person who used primary sources.

secularism the view that religious considerations should be kept separate from political affairs or public education.

social mobility the ability to move from one social class to another.

socialism an economic system in which the factors of production are owned by the public and operate for the welfare of all.

Strait of Hormuz a strait, or narrow channel of water, connecting the Persian Gulf and the Gulf of Oman.

thematic maps maps that focus on a specific idea, such as vegetation, natural resources, or historical trends.

Tigris and Euphrates river valley area in Southwest Asia along the Tigris and Euphrates rivers where the earliest Asian civilization arose about 3000 B.C. The area is also referred to as Mesopotamia and the Fertile Crescent.

totalitarianism government control over every aspect of public and private life.

validity truth or soundness.

Western civilization civilization that has its origins in ancient Greek and Roman civilizations.

Yellow (Huang He) river valley area in China along the Huang He where an early civilization emerged about 2000 B.C.

Key Terms and Names continued

NAMES

Archimedes (287?–212 B.C.) Hellenistic scientist who estimated the value of pi and invented the compound pulley and Archimedean screw.

Boyle, Robert (1627–1691) Irish scientist who is considered the father of modern chemistry and is best known for his experiments on gases and for introducing new methods of identifying the chemical composition of substances.

Churchill, Winston (1874–1965) British prime minister who inspired the British to fight against Hitler in World War II and helped lead the Allies to victory.

Copernicus, Nicolaus (1473–1543) Polish astronomer who proposed the theory that the earth and other planets revolve around the sun.

Curie, Marie ((1867–1906) French chemist who conducted research on radioactivity.

Edison, Thomas (1847–1931) American inventor who developed practical electric lighting and the modern research laboratory.

Einstein, Albert (1879–1955) American scientist who proposed the theory of relativity.

Erastosthenes (276?–195? B.C.) Greek mathematician who found a way of estimating the circumference of the earth.

Fulton, Robert (1765–1815) American inventor who developed the first practical steamboat.

Galileo (1564–1642) Italian astronomer who first used a telescope to study the stars and who was persecuted for supporting Copernicus's theory that the sun was the center of the universe.

Gandhi, Mohandas (1869–1948) Indian political and religious leader who helped India gain its independence from Great Britain by a method of nonviolent resistance.

Hitler, Adolf (1889–1945) German dictator who initiated World War II and the Holocaust.

Lenin, Vladimir (1870–1924) Russian dictator who founded the Communist Party in Russia and established the world's first Communist Party dictatorship.

Mao Zedong (1893–1976) Chinese dictator who led the Communist revolution in China.

Mother Theresa (1910–1997) Roman Catholic nun from Macedonia who worked among the poor of Calcutta, India, and established an order of nuns to serve the poor.

Newton, Sir Isaac (1642–1727) English mathematician and scientist who formed the theory of universal gravitation.

Pasteur, Louis ((1822–1895) French chemist who invented the process of pasteurization.

Pope John Paul II (1920–) Leader of the Roman Catholic Church since 1978 and first Polish-born pope.

Pythagorus (580?–? B.C.) Greek philosopher and mathematician famous for the Pythagorean theorem.

Tutu, Desmond (1931–) South African leader in the antiapartheid struggle.

Watt, James (1736–1819) British inventor who improved the steam engine.

Wilson, Woodrow (1856–1924) American President during World War I.

Name _____ Date _____

Judeo-Christian and Greco-Roman Perspectives

Specific Objective: Analyze the similarities and differences in Judeo-Christian and Greco-Roman views of law, reason and faith, and duties of the individual.

Read the summary to answer the questions on the next page.

For much of human history, people have lived under the rule of kings or other rulers who held absolute power. A direct contrast is the system of **democracy**, in which people govern themselves through councils and agreed-upon laws. The earliest democracies arose in ancient Greece and Rome.

Ancient Greece had a (limited) form of **direct democracy**. In a direct democracy, citizens represent themselves directly at councils. Ancient Rome saw the rise of the **republic**—an indirect democracy in which citizens rule through representatives, whom they elect. Many countries today, including the United States, use the republic form of democracy.

Greco-Roman Views

- Citizens should **participate in government** by voting, debating in public, making laws, serving on juries, and holding office.
- The world has **natural laws**—patterns that can be discovered through reason and intellect, rather than superstition.
- Democracy can be protected by having **branches of government**:
    a legislative branch to make laws,
    an executive branch to approve laws,
    a judicial branch to resolve legal disputes.
- There should be **written law**.

The development of democracy was supported by Judeo-Christian ideas, which spread in two main ways:

- After the Jews were exiled from Israel in A.D. 70, they brought their beliefs with them to their new lands.
- As Christianity spread throughout the Roman Empire, especially in the A.D. 400s, it became the dominant religion in Europe.

Judeo-Christian Views

- Every person is born with **worth and dignity** because they were created by God.
- Every person has the **ability to choose** between doing good and doing wrong.
- Every person has the **responsibility to help** others in need and the community.

PRACTICE

CALIFORNIA CONTENT
STANDARD 10.1.1

Judeo-Christian and Greco-Roman Perspectives

Directions: Choose the letter of the *best* answer.

1 What was groundbreaking about the development of democracy?

A People were able to govern without using written laws.

B People were governed by councils, instead of by an absolute ruler.

C Democracy brought together religious faith and government.

D Democracy balanced power among religious leaders and kings.

2 A political system in which representatives are elected by the people follows the model of

A direct democracy.

B a republic.

C branches of government.

D Judeo-Christian tradition.

3 In the Greco-Roman view, the world is governed by natural laws that can be discovered through

A reason.

B tradition.

C faith.

D citizen participation.

4 In Judeo-Christian tradition, helping others in need should be the

A only duty of political leaders.

B sole mission of religion.

C responsibility of government.

D responsibility of every person.

5 Greco-Roman and Judeo-Christian traditions share an emphasis on

A prosperity.

B fair government.

C faith in one God.

D individual choice.

6 What was *one* means by which Greco-Roman and Judeo-Christian values spread throughout Europe in the first centuries A.D.?

A explorers in the Age of Discovery

B expansion of the Roman Empire

C missionaries building churches

D conversion by the sword in Africa

Name _____ Date _____

Western Political Ideas of Tyranny

Specific Objective: Trace the development of Western political ideas of rule of law and illegitimacy of tyranny, using selections from Plato's *Republic* and Aristotle's *Politics*.

Read the summary to answer the questions on the next page.

In ancient Greece, the word *tyrant* was used for any leader who took over a government. A tyrant typically won public support and then seized power. Only later did tyrant come to mean what it does today—a leader who takes power illegally and abuses that power.

Tyranny in ancient Greece could be seen as a step toward democracy because a tyrant often gained power with support of the people, while a king, for instance, did not. However, like a king, a tyrant held all of the power himself.

Ancient Greek thinkers known as **philosophers** ("lovers of wisdom") often considered how different forms of government, including tyranny, affected society. In *The Republic*, the philosopher **Plato** wrote that a tyrant becomes troublesome when he loves his power so much that he takes drastic measures to maintain it:

> "At first, in the early days of his power, [the tyrant] is full of smiles . . . [but later] he is always stirring up some war or other, in order that the people may require a leader."

—Plato, *The Republic*

In Plato's view, a central reason that a tyrant becomes a problem is that the ruler has too much freedom—freedom to do whatever he or she likes, without regard for law or reason. As a result, the ruler can become a danger to the people.

Plato's famous student, **Aristotle**, said that not only does a tyrant have too much power, but acts selfishly, ultimately acting against the will and the benefit of the people. Aristotle wrote, in *Politics*, that tyranny:

> ". . . is just that arbitrary power of an individual which is responsible to no one, and governs all . . . with a view to its own advantage, not to that of its subjects, and therefore against their will."

—Aristotle, *Politics*

The influence of ancient Greek philosophers, such as Plato and Aristotle, extended beyond their time. Because they used logic and reason to think about the world and debate new ideas, they created a spirit of questioning and choice that aided the development of **democracy**.

PRACTICE

CALIFORNIA CONTENT
STANDARD 10.1.2

Western Political Ideas of Tyranny

Directions: Choose the letter of the *best* answer.

1 In ancient Greece, the word *tyrant* referred to a leader who

  A took over the government.

  B ruled with cruelty.

  C lost the support of the people.

  D wanted to become a king.

2 According to ancient Greek philosophers, with whom did a tyrant share power?

  A the people

  B the aristocracy

  C a group of philosophers

  D nobody

3 What was the primary activity of a philosopher in ancient Greece?

  A criticizing the government

  B thinking about natural laws

  C working toward democracy

  D reforming the laws

4 Plato wrote that a tyrant can become dangerous because every tyrant has too much

  A freedom to rule.

  B material wealth.

  C popular support.

  D interest in war.

5 According to Aristotle, why does a tyrant govern against the will of the people?

  A Tyrants take power illegally.

  B The people wish to rebel against a tyrant.

  C The tyrant is primarily self-interested.

  D Many people ruled by the tyrant are slaves.

6 Ancient Greek philosophers helped the development of democracy by

  A expanding definitions of citizenship.

  B ending the rule of the tyrants.

  C writing a basic set of fair laws.

  D promoting reason and thought.

Name _____ Date _____

Influence of the U.S. Constitution on World Political Systems

Specific Objective: Consider the influence of the U.S. Constitution on political systems in the contemporary world.

Read the chart to answer the questions on the next page.

The U.S. Constitution has influenced political systems throughout the world. This chart shows how some of its fundamental principles have been enacted.

Principle	Definition	In the U.S. Constitution	In the World Today
Federalism	The national government and the state governments share power.	Powers are shared between the national government and the 50 state governments.	In South Africa, power is shared between the national government and the governments of the nine provinces.
Separation of Powers	Government roles are divided among different branches, with no one branch holding all the power.	There are three branches of government: legislative (Congress), executive (the president), and judicial (the courts).	South Korea has three branches of government: parliament, a court system, and a president.
Popular Sovereignty	The government gets its authority from the people and reflects their will.	The preamble says, "We the people of the United States… do ordain and establish this Constitution…" which indicates that government power comes from the people.	The Japanese Constitution begins by saying that the government's power comes from the people and shall be used by them for their own benefit.
Individual Rights	Liberties and privileges are guaranteed to each citizen.	The Bill of Rights guarantees freedom of speech, religion, the press, and other rights.	The United Nations Declaration of Human Rights says that "all human beings are born free and equal" and should have certain rights.

Name _____   Date _____

PRACTICE

CALIFORNIA CONTENT
STANDARD 10.1.3

Influence of the U.S. Constitution on World Political Systems

Directions: Choose the letter of the *best* answer.

"We, the Japanese people… do proclaim that sovereign power resides with the people and do firmly establish this Constitution."

—The Constitution of Japan, 1946

1   What principle is reflected in the quotation from the Japanese Constitution?

A   federalism

B   separation of powers

C   popular sovereignty

D   individual rights

2   The U.S. Constitution reflects the principle of federalism by

A   sharing power between the national and state governments.

B   dividing the government into three branches.

C   guaranteeing all citizens equal protection under the law.

D   granting voting rights to all citizens 18 years and older.

3   A new government based on the principle of popular sovereignty *must*

A   ensure freedom of speech for all citizens.

B   have a directly elected president or prime minister.

C   affirm the idea that its power comes from the people.

D   divide government roles among different branches.

4   The division of South Korea's government into three branches with distinct powers reflects the principle of

A   federalism.

B   separation of powers.

C   popular sovereignty.

D   individual rights.

5   What guarantees freedom of speech to U.S. citizens?

A   the preamble to the U.S. Constitution

B   the Bill of Rights

C   Article 1 of the U.S. Constitution

D   the United Nations Declaration of Human Rights

REVIEW

**CALIFORNIA CONTENT
STANDARD 10.2.1**

The Enlightenment and Democratic Revolution

Specific Objective: Compare the major ideas of philosophers and their effects on the democratic revolutions in England, the United States, France, and Latin America.

Read the summary to answer the questions on the next page.

The **Enlightenment**, an intellectual movement that spread from Europe to America in the 1700s, helped inspire democratic revolutions in Europe, the United States, and Latin America. Key enlightenment writers included **Locke, Montesquieu,** and **Rousseau**.

John Locke (England)

- People have **natural rights** to life, liberty, and the ownership of property.
- People form **governments to protect these rights**. Therefore, a government gets its **authority from the people** and should reflect their will.

Influence: Locke's ideas influenced **Thomas Jefferson**, the main author of the **Declaration of Independence**, the basis of the American Revolution. It stated that people have natural "unalienable rights" and that a government derives its power from the people.

Charles-Louis Montesquieu (France)

- Government should be kept under control though **separation of powers**—a division into independent parts so that no part has too much power.
- A way to guarantee balance is to have **three branches of government**:
  a **legislative branch** to make laws;
  an **executive branch** to carry out and enforce laws;
  a **judicial branch** to interpret laws.

Influence: Montesquieu's ideas influenced **James Madison**, sometimes called the father of the **U.S. Constitution** because of his many contributions at the 1787 Constitutional Convention. The constitution separates government powers into three branches.

Jean-Jacques Rousseau (France)

- A **social contract** exists between citizens and their government. In this contract, citizens accept certain rights and responsibilities, and grant the government the power to uphold those rights and responsibilities.

Influence: The ideas of Locke and Rousseau influenced Latin-American revolutionary leader **Simón Bolívar**. Bolívar fought to liberate his country, present-day **Venezuela**, from Spanish rule. He also led movements for **independence and democracy** in what are now the nations of **Bolivia, Colombia, Ecuador, Panama,** and **Peru**.

Name __Megan Anders__   Date _____

PRACTICE

CALIFORNIA CONTENT
STANDARD 10.2.1

The Enlightenment and Democratic Revolution

Directions: Choose the letter of the *best* answer.

1 The European intellectual movement that emphasized the responsibility of government to protect people's natural rights was called the

  A Glorious Revolution.

  B Reformation.

  (C) Enlightenment.

  D Great Awakening.

2 The phrase "natural rights" is original to and central to the writings of which philosopher?

  (A) John Locke

  B Charles-Louis Montesquieu

  C Jean-Jacques Rousseau

  D James Madison

3 The Declaration of Independence expresses the philosophy that the power of government comes from

  A God.

  (B) the people.

  C natural rights.

  D the Constitution.

4 Which statement *best* summarizes the role of government in the social contract?

  (A) Its basis is the rights and responsibilities of the people.

  B It has legislative, executive, and judicial responsibilities.

  C It guarantees life, liberty, and the ownership of property.

  D Its main purpose is to interpret laws.

5 What principle is *directly* reflected in the division of a government into three branches?

  A natural laws

  (B) separation of powers

  C the social contract

  D democracy and independence

6 The ideas of Locke and Rousseau influenced Simón Bolívar in his commitment to

  A maintain the peaceful rule of the Spanish king.

  B urge the Venezuelan government to separate into three branches.

  C negotiate a social contract between Spain and Latin America.

  (D) fight for democratic revolution in Latin America.

REVIEW

CALIFORNIA CONTENT
STANDARD 10.2.2

Documents of Democracy

Specific Objective: List the principles of the Magna Carta, the English Bill of Rights (1689), the American Declaration of Independence (1776), the French Declaration of Rights of Man and the Citizen (1789), and the U.S. Bill of Rights (1791).

Read the summary to answer the questions on the next page.

Because of their traditions as English citizens, American colonists expected to have the rights granted in England by the **Magna Carta** and the **English Bill of Rights**. However, they were often denied these rights, and tensions grew in the colonies, leading toward revolution. Many principles of the earlier British documents continued in the American **Declaration of Independence** and the **Bill of Rights** in the U.S. Constitution. In Europe, some of the same principles and traditions carried into the French **Declaration of Rights of Man and the Citizen**.

Magna Carta (1215, England)

- Limited the powers of the king
- Laid the basis for **due process of law**—law should be known and orderly
- Prohibited the king from taking property or taxes without consent of a council

English Bill of Rights (1689)

- Guaranteed free elections and frequent meetings of Parliament
- Forbade excessive fines and cruel punishment
- Gave people the right to complain to the king or queen in Parliament
- Established **representative government**—laws made by a group that acts for the people

American Declaration of Independence (1776)

- Said that all men are created equal and have the right to life, liberty, and the pursuit of happiness; these are **unalienable rights**—rights that government cannot take away
- Said that governments get their power from the consent of the governed—the idea of **popular sovereignty**

French Declaration of the Rights of Man and Citizen (1789)

- Said that "men are born and remain free and equal in rights"
- Said that the purpose of government is to protect "natural" rights, including "liberty, property, security, and resistance to oppression"
- Guaranteed freedom of speech and freedom of religion

U.S. Bill of Rights (1791)

- Guaranteed freedom of speech, freedom of religion, and freedom of the press
- Guaranteed due process of law, including protection from unfair imprisonment
- Guaranteed trial by jury; protected people from "cruel and unusual punishment"

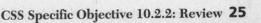

PRACTICE

CALIFORNIA CONTENT
STANDARD 10.2.2

Documents of Democracy

Directions: Choose the letter of the *best* answer.

1 Which of the following rights in the U.S. Bill of Rights comes from a provision in the Magna Carta?

A freedom of speech

B freedom of religion

C the right to life, liberty, and the pursuit of happiness

D the right to due process of law

2 Which statement *best* summarizes the idea of representative government as it was established in the English Bill of Rights?

A Powers not granted to the king are kept by the people.

B Laws are made and carried out by a group that acts for the people.

C All people are born free and equal in rights.

D A strong central government protects individual freedoms.

3 English colonists in America expected to have representative government in the colonies because

A there was a tradition of representative government in England.

B they fled England specifically to establish representative government.

C the king had promised the colonists representative government.

D most countries at that time had representative government.

4 The idea that governments get their power from the people they govern is called

A checks and balances.

B popular sovereignty.

C natural rights.

D states' rights.

5 The American Declaration of Independence and the French Declaration of the Rights of Man and Citizen *both*

A limit the power of the king.

B emphasize the rights of the individual.

C guarantee frequent meetings of Parliament.

D guarantee freedom of religion.

6 The term "unalienable rights" in the American Declaration of Independence refers to rights that

A immigrants do not possess.

B are guaranteed by written law.

C a government cannot take away.

D a government grants its people.

Name _____ Date _____

 REVIEW

CALIFORNIA CONTENT
STANDARD 10.2.3

The American Revolution

Specific Objective: Understand the unique character of the American Revolution, its spread to other parts of the world, and its continuing significance to other nations.

Read the summaries and time line to answer the questions on the next page.

The American Revolution was rooted in the belief that people possess natural rights and that government has a responsibility to protect those rights. American Patriots believed that the British government had violated their rights. As a result, they declared their independence from British rule and sought to create their own government.

Key Events in the American Revolution

1760s   American colonists protest unfair taxes and other rights violations by the British.

1775   War breaks out as shots are fired between colonists and British soldiers.

1776   American colonists issue a Declaration of Independence from British rule.

1781   British Army surrenders; Americans achieve independence.

1781–1787 States agree to a weak central government under the Articles of Confederation.

1787   States accept the U.S. Constitution, creating a stronger national government.

1791   The Bill of Rights is added to the U.S. Constitution.

Unique Success

The American Revolution ocurred during an era of revolutionary movements. Not all revolutions succeeded in creating stable democracy. For example, after the French Revolution in 1789, France descended into chaos, as people rebelled against many traditions. A dictatorship took over in 1799. By contrast, the American colonists rebelled mainly against British rule. After the revolution, they established laws that protected individual rights balanced with representative national and state governments.

Other Revolutionary Movements

The American Revolution was the first of a series of wars for independence that shared some common beliefs. Shared ideas included an emphasis on individual rights and the idea that a government's power comes from the people.

- French Revolution 1789–1799
- Haitian Revolution 1791–1802
- Batavian Revolution (Netherlands) 1795–1801
- Latin-American Wars for Independence
  (Venezuela, Bolivia, Colombia, and more) 1810–1824
- Greek war for independence 1821–1827

Name _____   Date _____

Directions: Choose the letter of the *best* answer.

1 A key issue that sparked the colonists to declare their independence from England was

   A the example of the French Revolution.

   B the issue of slavery.

   C concern for individual rights.

   D restrictions on immigration.

2 Which statement *best* describes the context in which the Declaration of Independence was issued?

   A The Declaration of Independence was issued, and then war broke out.

   B War broke out, and then the Declaration of Independence was issued.

   C The British army surrendered; then the Declaration of Independence was issued.

   D Americans achieved independence; then the Declaration of Independence was issued.

3 John Adams, second U.S. president, said that even before the War for Independence began, "The Revolution was in the hearts and minds of the people." What is the best way to paraphrase Adams's meaning?

   A The American people were eager for war.

   B Colonists had left England for the purpose of becoming revolutionaries.

   C Every colonist one day becomes a revolutionary.

   D The American Revolution was rooted in people's beliefs.

4 Which document was written before all the others?

   A Articles of Confederation

   B U.S. Constitution

   C Declaration of Independence

   D United States Bill of Rights

5 What is *one* reason that the American Revolution resulted in a stable democracy, while some other revolutions did not?

   A The United States rebelled against everything it had known.

   B The Articles of Confederation provided a period of transition from British rule.

   C Americans created both a strong government and protections for individual rights.

   D The Declaration of Independence legislated the ideals of equality and liberty.

6 What feature was shared by the major revolutionary movements of the late 1700s and early 1800s?

   A All maintained that government's power comes from its people.

   B All took place in colonized parts of the world.

   C Each ended with a bill of rights being passed by the new government.

   D Each began with a declaration of independence.

Name _____ Date _____

The French Revolution

Specific Objective: Explain how the ideology of the French Revolution led France to develop from a constitutional monarchy to democratic despotism to the Napoleonic empire.

Read the summary and cause-effect graphic to answer questions on the next page.

Like the American Revolution, the French Revolution of 1789 erupted after years of yearning for freedom and justice. Unlike the American Revolution, the revolutionary movement in France ended not in democracy but in dictatorship. Revolutionaries succeeded in overthrowing the French **Old Regime** that had divided the people into three unequal social classes, or **estates**. But old problems of poverty and injustice remained.

Revolutionaries could not agree on solutions and fought to keep control of the country. A period in the early 1790s was known as the **Reign of Terror** for the mass executions carried out by the revolutionary government's **Committee for Public Safety**. Meanwhile, poverty and chaos wearied the nation. Stability came only after the military leader **Napoleon Bonaparte** seized control as dictator in 1799. His powers as dictator led again to instability, however, continuing for generations. France did not adopt a constitution that guaranteed representative government until 1875.

Cause and Effect in the French Revolution

Injustice

Example: Absolute rule of **King Louis XVI** creates social and economic injustice; the king spends excessively and taxes the people heavily.

Revolution

Example: The **Third Estate**, the largest social class in France, names itself the National Assembly and takes over the government.

Uprising

Example: While the new government cannot agree on a constitution, **right-wing** nobles fight for return of the king and **left-wing** radicals take the law into their hands.

Repression

Example: **Napoleon Bonaparte** takes power; he accepts some revolutionary goals and restores order to a nation, but at the expense of individual rights.

Name _____ Date _____

PRACTICE

CALIFORNIA CONTENT
STANDARD 10.2.4

The French Revolution

Directions: Choose the letter of the *best* answer.

1 Among the causes of the French Revolution was the

A excessive spending of King Louis XVI.

B rise of the National Assembly.

C Reign of Terror.

D loss of the Old Regime.

2 In pre-Revolutionary France, estates were

A homes of noblemen.

B social classes.

C systems of taxation.

D clubs for radicals.

3 Who carried out the "Reign of Terror" in France?

A the Old Regime

B Napoleon Bonaparte

C the Third Estate

D the Committee for Public Safety

4 Which statement *best* describes the circumstances in which Napoleon Bonaparte took power?

A France was economically and politically secure.

B The Revolution was new and chaotic.

C There had been ten years of instability.

D The king had finally agreed to let Napoleon take power.

5 What form of government did Napoleon Bonaparte lead?

A democracy

B monarchy

C republic

D dictatorship

REVIEW

**CALIFORNIA CONTENT
STANDARD 10.2.5**

European Nationalism from Napoleon Until the Revolutions of 1848

Specific Objective: Discuss how nationalism spread across Europe with Napoleon but was repressed for a generation under the Congress of Vienna and Concert of Europe until the Revolutions of 1848.

Read the summaries to answer the questions on the next page.

After **Napoleon Bonaparte** seized control of France in 1799, he went on to expand his power across the continent. By 1812, he controlled much of Europe. However, many of the conquered lands rumbled with **nationalism**—loyalty to their own nations above all. Nationalists rose to throw off Napoleonic rule. As a result, Napoleon suffered a series of significant military defeats from 1812 to 1815, when his empire came to an end at the Battle of Waterloo.

The Congress of Vienna, 1814–1815

What and why: A series of international meetings to secure peace across Europe

Who: King Frederick William III of Prussia, Czar Alexander I of Russia, Emperor Francis I of Austria; foreign ministers from Britain and France; and, most importantly, **Klemens von Metternich**, foreign minister of Austria

- Countries around France were made stronger to **weaken France** and provide a **balance of power** across Europe.

- **Monarchies** that had been dethroned under Napoleon were **restored** and their **legitimacy**—hereditary right to rule—was proclaimed in France and elsewhere.

Concert of Europe, c. 1820–1853

What and why: An international alliance that met when peacekeeping issues arose

Who: the "Holy Alliance" of the **leaders of Russia, Austria, and Prussia**, led by Klemens von Metternich

- Royal rulers **promised to help each other in the event of revolution**.

Revolutions of 1848

What and why: Uprisings for self-government in France, the Austrian Empire, and the German and Italian states

Who: Nationalists who claimed loyalty to their fellow people rather than royal rulers

- Nationalists wanted **nation-states**—national governments that are independent from royal rule and serve the people and their ideals.

- Nationalists believed they would be united by their shared history, culture, and land rather than by any one ruler.

- The uprisings were quickly repressed, but their ideals persisted; within 20 years nationalist movements had turned the scattered states of **Germany and Italy** into two new, unified nation-states.

Name _____   Date _____

European Nationalism from Napoleon Until the Revolutions of 1848

Directions: Choose the letter of the *best* answer.

1. **Who was the *most* important European leader at the Congress of Vienna?**

   A   Napoleon Bonaparte

   B   King Frederick William III

   C   Czar Alexander I

   D   Klemens von Metternich

2. **Which statement is *true* of the outcome of the Congress of Vienna?**

   A   Its leaders created a balance of power in Europe.

   B   The French king was permanently exiled.

   C   Monarchy throughout Europe was weakened.

   D   The first nation-states were formed.

3. **What was the primary concern of the Concert of Europe?**

   A   Napoleonic control of Europe

   B   weakening the power in France

   C   the possibility of revolution

   D   the unification of Germany and Italy

4. **The Revolutions of 1848 had a lasting impact because they**

   A   proved nationalism had triumphed.

   B   were put down, but their ideals persisted.

   C   showed that nationalism had outlived its usefulness.

   D   all led to stable democracies.

5. **Which statement would an Austrian nationalist in the 1840s be *most* likely to make?**

   A   "My greatest loyalty is to my leader."

   B   "I believe in the legitimacy of the monarch."

   C   "The Holy Alliance is the key to our independence."

   D   "Our shared history and culture unite me with my people."

6. **Germany and Italy became two unified nation-states as a result of**

   A   the Congress of Vienna.

   B   the Concert of Europe.

   C   nationalist movements.

   D   the Holy Alliance.

REVIEW

CALIFORNIA CONTENT
STANDARD 10.3.1

The Industrial Revolution in England

Specific Objective: Analyze why England was the first country to industrialize.

Read the question-and-answers below. Then do the practice items on the next page.

The Industrial Revolution began in England in the mid-1700s. In the century that followed, factories and machines transformed the nation and spread throughout Europe and North America. Instead of using hand tools to make household quantities, people came to rely on machinery to produce large amounts of goods to be sold in shops.

Q: Why did the Industrial Revolution begin in England?

A: Economic Strength

- During the 1600s, overseas exploration had opened **new markets** for England, and led to a thriving economy based on **money**.
- British **merchants invested** money in new industries.
- New financial institutions such as **banks offered business loans** that helped spur industrial growth. The most famous was the powerful **Bank of England, 1694**.

A: Geography and Natural Resources

- England's **rivers** offered a dual advantage. Fast-flowing rivers were a source of water power to fuel machinery, and throughout the nation rivers provided inland transportation routes for industrial goods.
- In addition, England's excellent natural **harbors** were a benefit to merchant ships.
- England had rich natural resources in the form of **coal and iron mines**. Coal was a valuable source of energy to fuel machinery, and iron was used to make machines and products, such as tools and cookware.
- A region in west-central England became known as **the Black Country** for its smoke clouds from factories burning coal and smelting iron.

A: Population Growth

- Scientific improvements in farming during the 1700s led to more crops and healthier livestock—an **Agricultural Revolution** that brought more food to the people. Health and living conditions improved, and the population increased.
- A larger population meant **greater demand** for goods and more **available labor**.

A: Political Stability

- An isolated, island nation, England participated in European wars of the 18th and early 19th centuries, but never on home ground.
- England's industrial growth was **not interrupted by war**.

PRACTICE

CALIFORNIA CONTENT
STANDARD 10.3.1

The Industrial Revolution in England

Directions: Choose the letter of the *best* answer.

1 What was a *direct effect* of increased food production during Europe's Agricultural Revolution?

  A New markets opened.

  B Overseas trade increased.

  C The population increased.

  D Excess food was wasted.

2 During the 1600s, Europe developed a thriving economy based on

  A barter.

  B money.

  C banking.

  D factories.

3 A defining feature of Europe's Industrial Revolution was that many commercial goods were

  A purchased in overseas markets.

  B manufactured in less developed countries.

  C sold without economic barriers such as tariffs.

  D made by machine rather than by hand.

4 A geographic advantage of England in the Industrial Revolution was its

  A natural harbors.

  B national bank.

  C central location in Europe.

  D central mountain range.

5 The "Black Country" of England was known for its

  A forest fires.

  B smoke from coal.

  C fast-flowing rivers.

  D political stability.

6 What was *one* important power source for factories in 18th-century England?

  A gas

  B electricity

  C oil

  D water

Name _____ Date _____

Specific Objective: Examine how scientific and technological changes and new forms of energy brought about massive social, economic, and cultural change.

Read the chart and summaries to answer the questions on the next page.

Machinery made the Industrial Revolution possible. Reliance on machinery defined the revolution from its earliest days, and technological innovation drove its development. Here are some of the best-known innovations.

Technological Innovations of the Industrial Revolution		
Inventor	**Invention**	**Significance**
James Watt	Improved steam engine (1769)	Provided an efficient source of industrial power
Eli Whitney	Cotton gin (1793)	Sped cotton production by separating fiber from seed
Henry Bessemer	Bessemer process (1850s)	Quickly and cheaply made steel out of iron
Louis Pasteur	Pasteurization (sterilization) of liquids (1860s)	Increased the shelf life of milk and other products
Thomas Edison	Improved electric light (1879)	Made possible long-lasting indoor electric light

Spread of Technology

- By the 1840s, England had become a nation connected by **railroads**. Around the same time, the United States, Russia, and European nations, such as France and Germany, developed rail systems too. Railroads transported goods and linked commercial centers.

- Major advances in **communications** had occurred by the 1870s. International mail service had been achieved; telegraph messages could be transmitted around the world in minutes; and, in 1876, the telephone was used for the first time (though it did not become widespread until the early 1900s).

Effects on Society

- In agricultural life, the forces of weather and nature rule. In the new industrial culture, work could take place in any weather and more quickly than ever before.

- Railroads replaced horses, increasing loads and decreasing shipping and travel times. With the telegraph, it now took minutes rather than months for a message to reach a faraway destination. The pace of life had changed forever.

Name _____ Date _____

PRACTICE

CALIFORNIA CONTENT
STANDARD 10.3.2

Inventions and Social Change

Directions: Choose the letter of the *best* answer.

1 What impact did the steam engine have on the growth of industry?

A permitted merchants to reach new markets

B ended dependence on ocean transport

C reduced pollution compared with coal

D provided an efficient source of power

2 What technology did James Watt improve?

A the steam engine

B cotton processing

C electric light

D the Bessemer process

3 Which process would be an example of pasteurization?

A Milk is sterilized.

B Cotton fiber is separated.

C Coal is burned to make steam.

D Steel is made out of iron.

4 By the 1840s, England was connected by a network of

A craft guilds.

B telephone lines.

C railroads.

D electric lines.

5 Which 20th-century invention is *most* comparable to the telegraph in its impact?

A television

B e-mail and the Internet

C airplanes

D the telephone

6 Which increased as a result of the Industrial Revolution?

A prices for consumer goods

B dependence on the weather

C the speed of transactions

D isolation of commercial centers

Copyright © McDougal Littell/Houghton Mifflin Company

Name _____ Date _____

Population Shifts During the Industrial Revolution

Specific Objective: Describe the growth of population, rural to urban migration, and growth of cities associated with the Industrial Revolution.

Read the summary to answer the questions on the next page.

Population Growth

By the time of the Industrial Revolution, there were more people than ever before. A main reason for this was 18th century agricultural improvements, which all but ended the periodic famines that had kept down European populations. From 1750 to 1850, the population of England alone nearly tripled.

Rural to Urban Migration

Before the Industrial Revolution, most Europeans—and most of the world—lived on small farms in rural areas. By the mid-1800s, half the people in England lived in cities, and by 1900 this change had spread throughout much of Europe. Population migration from rural to urban settings is a defining feature of the Industrial Revolution.

Why Cities?

- Factory work made it necessary for many workers to be in one place.
- New goods brought the need for new market centers. Often, these were located on waterways for ease of transportation.
- The emerging banking and commercial industries developed their own centers.

Disease in Urban Centers

Nineteenth-century city dwellers were vulnerable to contagious—and sometimes deadly—diseases such as typhus, cholera, and influenza. These spread rapidly in the unhealthy conditions created by industrialization.

Cause	→	Effect/Cause	→	Effect
Cheaply built, overcrowded housing	→	Poor living conditions	→	
Industrial pollution	→	Polluted air and water	→	**SPREAD OF DISEASE**
Terrible sanitation	→	Streets full of waste; contaminated water	→	

Name _____ Date _____

PRACTICE

CALIFORNIA CONTENT
STANDARD 10.3.3

Population Shifts During the Industrial Revolution

Directions: Choose the letter of the *best* answer.

Use the graph to answer questions 1–3.

Population Growth of Five Cities

BIRMINGHAM
1800 𝕏𝕏𝕏𝕏𝕏𝕏
1850 𝕏𝕏𝕏𝕏𝕏𝕏𝕏𝕏𝕏𝕏𝕏𝕏𝕏𝕏𝕏𝕏
𝕏𝕏𝕏𝕏𝕏𝕏𝕏𝕏𝕏𝕏𝕏𝕏𝕏𝕏𝕏𝕏

𝕏 = 10,000 people

LIVERPOOL
1800 𝕏𝕏𝕏𝕏𝕏𝕏
1850 𝕏𝕏𝕏𝕏𝕏𝕏𝕏𝕏𝕏𝕏𝕏𝕏𝕏𝕏𝕏𝕏𝕏𝕏𝕏𝕏𝕏𝕏𝕏𝕏𝕏𝕏𝕏𝕏
𝕏𝕏𝕏𝕏𝕏𝕏𝕏𝕏𝕏𝕏𝕏

LONDON
1800 𝕏𝕏𝕏𝕏𝕏𝕏𝕏𝕏𝕏𝕏𝕏𝕏𝕏𝕏𝕏𝕏𝕏𝕏𝕏𝕏𝕏𝕏𝕏𝕏𝕏𝕏
𝕏𝕏𝕏𝕏𝕏𝕏𝕏𝕏𝕏𝕏𝕏𝕏𝕏𝕏𝕏𝕏𝕏𝕏𝕏𝕏𝕏𝕏𝕏𝕏𝕏𝕏
𝕏𝕏𝕏𝕏𝕏𝕏𝕏𝕏𝕏𝕏𝕏𝕏𝕏𝕏𝕏𝕏𝕏𝕏𝕏𝕏𝕏𝕏𝕏𝕏𝕏𝕏
𝕏𝕏𝕏𝕏𝕏𝕏𝕏𝕏𝕏𝕏𝕏𝕏𝕏𝕏𝕏𝕏𝕏𝕏𝕏𝕏𝕏𝕏𝕏𝕏𝕏
1850 𝕏𝕏𝕏𝕏𝕏𝕏𝕏𝕏𝕏𝕏𝕏𝕏𝕏𝕏𝕏𝕏𝕏𝕏𝕏𝕏𝕏𝕏𝕏𝕏𝕏𝕏
𝕏𝕏𝕏𝕏𝕏𝕏𝕏𝕏𝕏𝕏𝕏𝕏𝕏𝕏𝕏𝕏𝕏𝕏𝕏𝕏𝕏𝕏𝕏𝕏𝕏𝕏
𝕏𝕏𝕏𝕏𝕏𝕏𝕏𝕏𝕏𝕏𝕏𝕏𝕏𝕏𝕏𝕏𝕏𝕏𝕏𝕏𝕏𝕏𝕏𝕏𝕏𝕏
𝕏𝕏𝕏𝕏𝕏𝕏𝕏𝕏𝕏𝕏𝕏𝕏𝕏𝕏𝕏𝕏𝕏𝕏𝕏𝕏𝕏𝕏𝕏𝕏𝕏𝕏
𝕏𝕏𝕏𝕏𝕏𝕏𝕏𝕏𝕏𝕏𝕏𝕏𝕏𝕏𝕏𝕏𝕏𝕏𝕏𝕏𝕏𝕏𝕏𝕏𝕏𝕏
𝕏𝕏𝕏𝕏𝕏𝕏𝕏𝕏𝕏𝕏𝕏𝕏𝕏𝕏𝕏𝕏𝕏𝕏𝕏𝕏𝕏𝕏𝕏𝕏𝕏𝕏
𝕏𝕏𝕏𝕏𝕏𝕏𝕏𝕏𝕏𝕏𝕏𝕏𝕏𝕏𝕏𝕏𝕏𝕏𝕏𝕏𝕏𝕏𝕏𝕏𝕏𝕏
𝕏𝕏𝕏𝕏𝕏𝕏𝕏𝕏𝕏𝕏𝕏𝕏

EDINBURGH
1800 𝕏𝕏𝕏𝕏𝕏
1850 𝕏𝕏𝕏𝕏𝕏𝕏𝕏𝕏𝕏𝕏𝕏𝕏𝕏𝕏𝕏𝕏

GLASGOW
1800 𝕏𝕏𝕏𝕏𝕏𝕏𝕏𝕏
1850 𝕏𝕏𝕏𝕏𝕏𝕏𝕏𝕏𝕏𝕏𝕏𝕏𝕏𝕏𝕏𝕏𝕏𝕏𝕏𝕏𝕏𝕏𝕏𝕏𝕏𝕏
𝕏𝕏𝕏𝕏𝕏𝕏𝕏

1 Between 1800 and 1850, London's population

A doubled.

B more than doubled.

C grew at the same rate as Liverpool.

D grew faster than Liverpool's.

2 Which city had the *smallest* population throughout 1800–1850?

A Birmingham

B Liverpool

C Edinburgh

D Glasgow

3 What is the *best* explanation for the population growth shown in the graph?

A An agricultural revolution meant there was more food available.

B Better mining techniques increased the demand for coal.

C Cities provided better entertainment and cultural opportunities.

D Cities were more sanitary and healthy environments than farms.

Name _____ Date _____

The Evolution of Work and Labor

Specific Objective: Trace the evolution of work and labor, including the demise of the slave trade and the effects of immigration, mining and manufacturing, division of labor, and the union movement.

Read the summary to answer the questions on the next page.

The Industrial Revolution quickened the pace of workers' lives and shaped how they worked and where they lived. No longer did the vast majority work in agriculture. Millions were employed in **mining** and **manufacturing**—many working in a cash economy for the first time and in fast-growing urban centers.

The Demise of the Slave Trade

The Industrial Revolution was financed in part by profits from the trans-Atlantic slave trade. But industry soon became more profitable than the slave trade. During the early 1800s, the slave trade was abolished in England, the United States, and much of Europe.

Debates about the economic benefits of slavery developed alongside the obvious moral questions. Especially in the industrial northern United States, many people felt that **free labor**—not slave labor—was the only way to grow a strong industrial economy.

Immigration

Immigration fueled the labor force, especially in North America. In the 19th century, expanding industry in North America drew millions of **immigrants from Europe and Asia** who sought new economic opportunities. By the 1870s, they arrived at a rate of more than 2,000 a day.

Advances in **transportation** made this mass migration possible. Overseas transportation was safer and more available than ever before, and immigrants traveled within North America by the new railway systems.

Division of Labor

Increasingly divided social classes emerged during the Industrial Revolution. Very wealthy industrial owners and businessmen formed the **upper class**. The **middle classes** included a variety of professionals, such as teachers, lawyers, shopkeepers, and small businessmen. Factory workers and other dependent laborers made up the **working class**.

The Union Movement

The union movement arose to address the many problems faced by laborers. A **union** is an organization that speaks for the workers it represents. Its first effort to solve a problem is often **collective bargaining**—negotiations, led by the union, to resolve disputes between workers and employers. If this effort is unsuccessful, it may be followed by a **strike**, in which union members refuse to work until their demands are met.

Name _____   Date _____

The Evolution of Work and Labor

Directions: Choose the letter of the *best* answer.

1 Which would have been a *common* life change in England during the Industrial Revolution?

  A A farmer moves to an industrial area to work in a coal mine.

  B A coal miner works his way up through the ranks to own the mine.

  C A coal miner moves to the country to run his own farm.

  D A lawyer loses his business and is forced to work in a coal mine.

2 In Great Britain, the Factory Act of 1819 declared it illegal for children to work more than 12 hours a day. What does the act suggest about labor conditions at that time?

  A Working conditions were worse in Great Britain than in other nations.

  B The government frequently intervened on behalf of workers.

  C Some children spent more than half of each day working.

  D Factories were unable to attract adult employees.

3 In the 19th century, millions of people seeking work migrated

  A from Asia to Europe.

  B from North America to Europe.

  C from North America to Europe and Asia.

  D from Asia and Europe to North America.

4 Which statement is *true* of social class during the Industrial Revolution?

  A People could move freely from one social class to another.

  B Social classes became increasingly divided.

  C The very idea of social classes became outdated.

  D Europe was generally divided between an upper class and a working class.

5 Collective bargaining was a process of negotiation between

  A employers and workers.

  B employers and the government.

  C unions and the government.

  D workers and unions.

6 In 1902, Pennsylvania coal miners refused to work, returning to their jobs only when guaranteed a 10 percent pay increase and reduction of hours. The miners' action is an example of

  A forming a union.

  B free labor.

  C a strike.

  D a picket.

Name _____ Date _____

Components of an Industrial Economy

Specific Objective: Understand the connections among natural resources, entrepreneurship, labor, and capital in an industrial economy.

Read the graphic organizer to answer the questions on the next page.

Components of an Industrial Economy

Entrepreneurship

Entrepreneurs are people who organize new businesses by deciding how the business will be run and what it will produce, and then
1) obtaining money from lenders and investors
2) using the money to obtain necessary resources

NECESSARY RESOURCES

Natural Resources	**Capital**	**Labor**
Products of nature, such as minerals and land	Human-made resources such as machinery and tools	People who perform work

INDUSTRIAL PRODUCTION

Consumer Goods

Goods that are sold to consumers

Name _____   Date _____

Components of an Industrial Economy

Directions: Choose the letter of the *best* answer.

Use the quotation to answer questions 1 and 2.

> "They are the leaders on the way to material progress. . . . They guess what the consumers would like to have and are intent on providing them with these things."
>
> —from *Human Action: A Treatise on Economics,* Ludwig von Mises

1 The quotation describes the role in an industrial economy played by

   A entrepreneurs.

   B investors.

   C labor.

   D salespeople.

2 According to the quotation, what skill is important to a business leader?

   A the ability to raise money

   B an understanding of people's needs

   C fair leadership

   D a love of material goods

3 What is the goal of industrial production?

   A employment for great numbers of people

   B efficient use of natural resources

   C finding new sources of capital

   D the manufacture of consumer goods that can be sold

4 Which event in 19th-century England *most* benefited its industrial economy?

   A war against Russia

   B the growth of democracy

   C increased population growth

   D a decline in agriculture

5 Which social change in 19th-century England would have *most* benefited an industrial entrepreneur?

   A the movement toward a national education system

   B abolition of the slave trade

   C greater availability of bank loans

   D laws to protect laborers

Name _____ Date _____

Specific Objective: Analyze the emergence of capitalism as a dominant economic pattern and the responses to it, including Utopianism, Social Democracy, Socialism, and Communism.

Read the summaries to answer the questions on the next page.

Capitalism is an economic system that emphasizes profit and private ownership. In capitalism, the **factors of production**—such as land and other natural resources—are owned privately, by wealthy business owners and investors. Critics of capitalism say that the system creates profit for owners and investors, but not for workers. During the Industrial Revolution, many workers labored in poverty and under dangerous conditions. New systems of thought arose in response to such problems:

Utopianism

Basic idea: people live and work together, sharing goods and property.

- Utopian communities were alternative societies based on cooperation and sharing. A number of these communities were founded in the United States in the early 1800s. Most were formed by small groups of people in rural areas and did not last for long. But a few, such as the Amana colonies in Iowa, were sizable and existed for more than a century.

Socialism

Basic idea: the factors of production are owned by the people, at least in part, and are used for the benefit of all.

- Many socialists believed that capitalism was a cause of moral and ethical problems, such as child labor and low wages. They thought people could work together to solve these problems and plan for a more fair economy. Nineteenth-century socialists played important roles in the labor movement.

Communism

Basic idea: workers should take control of all the factors of production.

- Communism is a type of socialism that is often associated with revolution. The term "communism" became famous in the book *Communist Manifesto* by Karl Marx and Friedrich Engels, published in 1848. Marx and Engels emphasized revolutionary struggle as a means of achieving a society in which all people were economically equal.

Social Democracy

Basic idea: government plays a role in managing production and provides certain social services.

- Social democrats believe that the government should play a role in the economy in order to make sure that the people receive certain benefits, such as health care and education. Social democracy developed in the 20th century out of socialist ideas. It is the dominant system in many European nations today.

Name _____ Date _____

Directions: Choose the letter of the *best* answer.

1 **Which statement would a critic of capitalism have *most* likely made during the Industrial Revolution?**

   A "Rapid economic growth destroys our natural resources."

   B "Most of our consumer goods are produced overseas."

   C "Business owners get rich while workers remain poor."

   D "The cost of machinery and new factories is too high."

2 **Nineteenth-century socialists made significant gains in**

   A the United States Congress.

   B the labor movement.

   C abolitionism.

   D halting the Industrial Revolution.

3 **What was the relationship between work and property in a utopian community?**

   A Those who worked the most owned the most property.

   B A few owned most of the property while others worked for them.

   C People worked separately but shared their property.

   D People worked together and shared their property.

4 **With what economic idea is Karl Marx *most* closely associated?**

   A capitalism

   B socialism

   C communism

   D social democracy

5 **Citizens in a social democracy expect their government to**

   A provide them with certain benefits.

   B leave the economy alone.

   C own all the factors of production.

   D engage in collective bargaining.

6 **Which economic system emerged in Europe as a response to *both* capitalist and socialist ideals?**

   A socialism

   B communism

   C trade unionism

   D social democracy

Name _____ Date _____

Romanticism in Art and Literature

Specific Objective: Describe the emergence of Romanticism in art and literature (e.g., the poetry of William Blake and William Wordsworth), social criticism (e.g., the novels of Charles Dickens), and the move away from Classicism in Europe.

Read the summary to answer the questions on the next page.

Nineteenth-century European art, music, and literature were dominated by two styles: classicism and romanticism.

- **Classicism** sought to imitate the arts of ancient Greece and Rome. Tradition, reason, and symmetry were prized. The forms of plays and musical compositions followed particular rules; painters and architects incorporated subjects and images from the ancient world.

- **Romanticism** emphasized love of nature, emotional expression, individual experience, and the importance of ordinary people and folk traditions. Often, romantics longed for a simpler, gentler past—a time when noble people lived in harmony with unspoiled nature—a past that did not in fact exist. Romanticism developed in the early 1800s and became widely popular. In some ways, Romanticism reflected the spirit and concerns of its time.

While across Europe . . .	. . . romanticism celebrated . . .	Example
. . . people demanded more political power from their royal rulers, . . .	. . . the value of ordinary people.	William Wordsworth wrote poetry that used the language of ordinary people.
. . . industrialization caused pollution, and people left rural areas for cities, . . .	. . . the beauty of nature.	Beethoven's *Pastoral* symphony expressed his love of nature.

Romanticism's focus on the value of ordinary people and their experiences led to the development of **social criticism**—artistic work that identifies and expresses concern for problems in society. The fiction of Charles Dickens was known for its social criticism. In *A Christmas Carol*, for instance, Dickens vividly describes the sufferings of the poor.

Name _____ Date _____

Romanticism in Art and Literature

Directions: Choose the letter of the *best* answer.

"How glad I am to be able to roam in wood and thicket, among the trees and flowers and rocks!"

—Ludwig van Beethoven

1 What Romantic value is expressed in Beethoven's words about nature?

  A scientific knowledge

  B personal experience

  C the ability to travel

  D the diversity of life

2 Which would have been the *most* likely subject for a classical painter?

  A a farmer milking a cow

  B folk dancing

  C ancient Greek philosophers

  D a sunset over magnificent mountains

3 Nineteenth-century European Romantics tended to view the past as a

  A time of ignorance.

  B time best forgotten.

  C more stimulating time.

  D gentler time.

4 European Romanticism celebrated the beauty of nature at a time when

  A people were traveling to remote areas for the first time.

  B industrialization was polluting the land.

  C agriculture was undergoing a revival.

  D outdoor recreation had gained in popularity.

5 European Romanticism celebrated ordinary people at a time when they

  A lived in democracies.

  B showed little interest in politics.

  C demanded their rights.

  D idealized the nobility.

6 A 19th-century novel that attempted "social criticism" might have shown how a young hero or heroine was affected by

  A a week at the seashore.

  B growing up in a loving family.

  C being educated in the arts.

  D industrial pollution.

Name _____ Date _____

Industrial Economies and the Rise of Imperialism

Specific Objective: Describe the rise of industrial economies and their link to imperialism and colonialism.

Read the summary to answer the questions on the next page.

Beginning around 1850, European nations took control of much of Africa, Asia, and Latin America. The policy of a powerful nation dominating the politics, economy, and society of another nation is known as **imperialism**.

- European imperialism went hand-in-hand with **industrialization**; European nations sought raw materials and new markets for industry and used new forms of transportation and weaponry to seize foreign lands.

- European leaders often justified their imperialism partly through the theory of **Social Darwinism**—the application of Darwin's ideas about the "survival of the fittest" to social change. Social Darwinists believe that wealth, technology, success, and strength make some groups superior to others, thus giving Europeans the right to invade some non-European lands.

Causes
Nationalism: To gain power, European nations compete for colonies, particularly in areas that permit control of trade routes.
Economic competition: Industrial demand for natural resources and new markets spurs a search for colonies.
Racism: A prevailing belief in the late 1800s holds that Europeans are a superior race, and have a right to claim lands inhabited by non-European people.
Missionary impulse: Missionaries and many Christian leaders in Europe believed they would do good by spreading their Christian teachings throughout the globe.

IMPERIALISM
Europeans of the late 1800s and early 1900s use their wealth and advantage to conquer foreign lands and influence the economies, politics, and social lives of the colonized.

Effects
Colonization: Stronger nations, in this case in Europe, control distant lands and people—in the 1800s, areas of Africa, Asia, and Latin America.
Colonial economics: Europeans control trade in the colonies and set up local economies that are dependent on the Europeans.
Christianization: Christianity spreads to Africa, India, and Asia.

Name _____ Date _____

Industrial Economies and the Rise of Imperialism

Directions: Choose the letter of the *best* answer.

1 Which event would be an example of imperialism?

A   A powerful nation seizes control of a poor nation and its resources.

B   Laborers in a poor nation are employed seasonally by a powerful nation.

C   Powerful nations join together to form a trade network.

D   A poor nation receives economic aid from a powerful nation.

2 Nineteenth-century European imperialism was spurred in part by success in

A   cartography (map-making).

B   technology and industry.

C   the teaching of foreign languages.

D   agriculture.

3 What geography-related goal *most* motivated 19th-century European imperialists?

A   exploration of major waterways

B   exploration of inland areas

C   discovery of shorter trade routes

D   control of trade routes

4 The resource of central Africa that would have been *most* attractive to 19th-century European imperialists was its

A   workforce.

B   waterways.

C   copper mines.

D   wildlife.

5 Christian missionaries in colonized lands, in the 1800s,

A   wanted people in other lands to become Christians.

B   traveled to learn about religion in other lands.

C   fought to stop the spread of imperialism.

D   worked to help people forget about imperialism.

6 A 19th-century English Social Darwinist would say that his or her nation's power was proof of

A   the success of democracy.

B   the scientific revolution.

C   its superiority.

D   its religious faith.

Name _____ Date _____

REVIEW

Locations of Colonial Rule

Specific Objective: Discuss the locations of the colonial rule of such nations as England, France, Germany, Italy, Japan, the Netherlands, Russia, Spain, Portugal, and the United States.

Read the chart and summary to answer the questions on the next page.

Locations of 19th-Century Colonial Rule			
Colonizing Nation	**In Africa?**	**In Asia?**	**In South America?**
Great Britain	X	X	X
France	X	X	X
Germany	X	X	
Italy	X		
Japan		X	
The Netherlands		X	X
Belgium	X		
Spain	X		X
Portugal	X		X
The United States		X	

- **Great Britain** colonized more land than any other nation, controlling parts of Europe, Asia, Africa, North America, and South America and all of Australia

- In 1800, **South America** was controlled mainly by the Spanish and the Portuguese. Most of that continent achieved independence by 1830.

- At the **Berlin Conference of 1884–1885**, 14 European countries met to divide up the continent of **Africa**. Great Britain and France claimed most of it. The remainder was divided among Germany, Italy, Belgium, Spain, and Portugal, with only 3.4 percent left independent. The Netherlands had no African colony.

- The United States acquired the Asian island nation of the **Philippines** in 1898 and used it mainly for sugar crops. (The Philippines achieved independence in 1946.)

Name _____   Date _____

PRACTICE

Locations of Colonial Rule

Directions: Choose the letter of the *best* answer.

1 What *two* European nations colonized *most* of South America?

   A England and Spain

   B England and France

   C Spain and France

   D Spain and Portugal

2 What *two* European nations colonized *most* of Africa?

   A England and Spain

   B England and France

   C Spain and France

   D Spain and Portugal

3 During the late 1800s, which European nation had *no* colony in Africa?

   A Belgium

   B Germany

   C Italy

   D The Netherlands

4 Which European nation colonized the *most* land around the world during the 19th century?

   A France

   B Germany

   C Great Britain

   D Spain

5 The purpose of the Berlin Conference was to plan for the

   A independence of South America.

   B conquest of China.

   C division of Africa.

   D control of international trade routes.

6 Where did the United States acquire a colony in 1898?

   A Africa

   B Asia

   C South America

   D The Caribbean

Name _____ Date _____

Responses to Colonialism

Specific Objective: Explain imperialism from the perspectives of colonizers and colonized; explain immediate and long-term responses by people under colonial rule.

Read the case-study chart and summary to answer the questions on the next page.

During the late 19th and early 20th centuries, European imperialists claimed and colonized lands throughout Africa and Asia. They brought with them beliefs that profoundly affected the people whose lands they colonized.

European Colonization in Africa: A Case-Study of Colonialism	
European colonists in Africa believed . . .	**As a result, Africans . . .**
. . . wealth and power gave them the right to claim foreign lands.	. . . lost their lands and their independence.
. . . European economies and technology would benefit colonized people.	. . . had traditional economies replaced by capitalism; lost control of trade networks.
. . . European medicine and education would benefit colonized people.	. . . had longer life spans and higher literacy rates in some areas.
. . . European culture would benefit colonized people.	. . . had their traditional cultures and leaders repressed.
. . . Europeans were racially superior	. . . were treated as inferior.

African colonial resistance was difficult to attempt. European colonizers typically refused to engage in diplomacy with African rulers, and European weaponry made them formidable opponents. However, when European power weakened after World War I, African nationalism rose. Ghana, proclaimed a British colony in 1874, struggled for independence for many years. In 1925 legislative council elections were held. Nationalist political parties formed in the 1940s. In 1952, when Kwame Nkrumah became prime minister, he was the first black African leader in the area in more than 50 years. Ghana achieved independence in 1957. Other African nations tried various forms of resistance.

Form of Resistance	Example
Conflict against colonial invaders	Ashanti battles against British invaders, 1800s; Libya battles against Italian invaders, 1911–1932
Conflict against colonial rulers	Maji Maji uprising in East Africa, 1905
Guerrilla warfare	Mau Mau uprising in Kenya, 1952–1956
Labor unions, strikes, boycotts	Nationalist political parties in Ghana, 1940s–1950s

Name _____   Date _____

Responses to Colonialism

Directions: Choose the letter of the *best* answer.

1 European colonists believed they had the right to colonize Africa because

   A Europeans had wealth and power.

   B Africa had no trade networks.

   C Africans did not resist.

   D Europeans had no colonies.

2 For Africans, European colonization resulted in

   A more wealth and power, less education.

   B expanded control of trade networks and emphasis on traditional economies.

   C loss of lands, loss of trade, some gains in health and literacy.

   D more local leadership and stronger traditional cultures.

3 What event closely preceded the rise of African nationalist movements?

   A The slave trade came to dominate the coast.

   B African kingdoms were destroyed.

   C Great Britain claimed West Africa as its colony.

   D World War I ended.

4 The African prime minister who first came to power in Ghana

   A was the area's first African leader since the early 1900s.

   B was appointed by British colonialists.

   C showed that Ghana had achieved independence.

   D showed that African nationalism had no effect.

5 Ghana achieved independence

   A after a long and bloody revolution.

   B by quickly overthrowing the colonial government.

   C in a series of steps.

   D at the same time as many other African nations.

Name _____ Date _____

Struggles for Independence from Colonialism

Specific Objective: Describe the independence struggles of the colonized regions of the world, including the roles of leaders, such as Sun Yat-sen in China, and the roles of ideology and religion.

Read the summary to answer the questions on the next page.

Haiti (then called Saint Domingue)

Achieved independence: from France, 1804

Key leader: Toussaint L'Ouverture, a formerly enslaved African, was a self-taught leader

Ideology: Enslaved Africans—the overwhelming majority of the population—should rebel to gain their own freedom and independence for their nation.

- Haiti became the first black republic in the world, and the second nation—after the United States—to win independence from colonial rule.

South America

Achieved independence: from Spain by 14 nations, 1809–1825

Key leader: Simón Bolívar, a **creole**—a Spaniard born in South America; this highly educated class produced many revolutionary leaders

Ideology: Military power will liberate South America from unjust rule by Europe.

- The military leadership of Bolívar and fellow general José de San Martín defeated Spanish troops in a series of decisive battles.

China

Achieved independence: from the Qing Dynasty (a military empire), 1911

Key leader: Sun-Yat Sen, attended school in Hawaii, where he learned about western government and economics and came to admire Abraham Lincoln.

Ideology: Three Principles of the People, which translate roughly to freedom from imperialism; a government based on a constitution by the people; and a healthy economy to provide for the people .

- Sun-Yat Sen became the first president of the republic of China.

India

Achieved independence: from Great Britain, 1947

Key leader: Mohandas Karamchand Gandhi, a Hindu like the majority of Indians, was greatly respected as a leader because of his deep religious faith.

Ideology: civil disobedience—the choice to disobey an unjust law, in public and in a spirit of nonviolence

- India took back control from the British in a series of steps, beginning in 1919.

Name _____ Date _____

PRACTICE

CALIFORNIA CONTENT
STANDARD 10.4.4

Struggles for Independence from Colonialism

Directions: Choose the letter of the *best* answer.

"The British treat nations as the silk-worm farmer treats his worms; as long as they produce silk, he cares for them well; when they stop, he feeds them to the fish."

—from *The Vital Problem of China (1917)*, Sun Yat-sen

1 **Which statement *best* summarizes the danger Sun Yat-sen describes in the quotation?**

A Revolution brings with it the possibility of total destruction.

B European rulers are cruel and unpredictable.

C Imperialists care not for their subjects, but only for their own gain.

D Agricultural production cannot guarantee economic security.

2 **What made the Haitian revolution a landmark in history?**

A At that time, no other nation had won independence from colonial rule.

B Enslaved people won their freedom and established a republic.

C Its leaders were highly educated.

D It was achieved through civil disobedience.

3 **Struggles for independence in Latin America were led mainly by**

A Toussaint L'Ouverture.

B the Spanish.

C enslaved people.

D creoles.

4 **What was the *primary* means through which Indians sought independence from Great Britain?**

A nonviolent civil disobedience

B a quick and bloodless takeover

C military strength in combat

D secret resistance movements

5 **From whom did the Chinese win independence in 1911?**

A the Ming dynasty

B the Qing dynasty

C Great Britain

D Japan

Copyright © McDougal Littell/Houghton Mifflin Company

54 CSS Specific Objective 10.4.4: Practice

REVIEW

CALIFORNIA CONTENT
STANDARD 10.5.1

Factors Leading to World War I

Specific Objective: Analyze the arguments for entering into war presented by leaders from all sides of the Great War. Analyze the role of political and economic rivalries, ethnic and ideological conflicts, domestic discontent and disorder, and propaganda and nationalism in mobilizing the civilian population in support of "total war."

Read the chart and summaries to answer questions on the next page.

Competition Among Nations—Late 1800s	
Rivalry	**Example**
Competition for markets and materials	Germany competed with Great Britain, Europe's industrial leader.
Competition for colonies in Africa and Asia; imperialism	Great Britain was the leader in the race for colonies. Germany and France each sought to control Morocco, in northern Africa.
Competition for European territory	Austria-Hungary and Russia vied for influence in the Balkans.

The Rise of Nationalism and Militarism—**Nationalism**, a deep devotion to one's own nation, fueled competition. It also encouraged the growth of **militarism**, the policy of glorifying military power and keeping an army prepared for war. In the 1890s, many European nations began building large armies.

The Alliance System—Each nation was required to support its allies. A conflict between any two countries could draw everyone into war. The Great Powers formed two alliances.

- In 1907, the **Triple Alliance** was composed of Austria-Hungary, Germany, and Italy. By 1915, the Ottoman Turks and Bulgaria had joined and it became known as the **Central Powers**.

- In 1907, the **Triple Entente** was composed of France, Great Britain, and Russia. Italy joined in 1915; the United States in 1917. These countries became the **Allies**.

The "Powder Keg" Leads to Total War—The Balkan Peninsula was called the "powder keg" of Europe because of its more than 400 years of ethnic and political conflict. After the Balkan Wars of 1912–1913, Serbia, a mostly Slavic country, nearly doubled its territory. Russia, also a largely Slavic country, supported Serbian expansion. Austria and Germany did not.

The Powder Keg Ignites in 1914

- **June 28**—Archduke Franz Ferdinand—heir to the Austria-Hungary throne—is killed by a Serbian nationalist in Bosnia, an Austro-Hungarian province.

- **July 28**—Austria-Hungary declares war on Serbia. Russia mobilizes to aid Serbia.

- **August 1**—Germany, an ally of Austria-Hungary, declares war on Russia.

- **August 3**—Germany declares war on France, Russia's ally.

- **August 4**—Germany tries to invade France through neutral Belgium. Great Britain, France's ally, declares war on Germany.

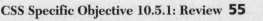

PRACTICE

CALIFORNIA CONTENT
STANDARD 10.5.1

Factors Leading to World War I

Directions: Choose the letter of the *best* answer.

1 "Nationalism" is *best* defined as

   A belief in private property.

   B desire for territories overseas.

   C strong devotion to one's country.

   D support for a strong army.

2 Which countries made up the Triple Entente in 1907?

   A Austria-Hungary, Sweden, and Russia

   B The United States, Germany, and Russia

   C Great Britain, France, and Russia

   D Belgium, Germany, and France

3 Why were the Balkans known as the "powder keg" of Europe in the early 1900s?

   A Several large explosions had taken place in its factories.

   B It had endured more than 400 years of ethnic and political conflict.

   C It produced both weapons and gun powder.

   D It had an unusual geographic shape that others wished to change.

4 The assassination of which leader led to the outbreak of World War I?

   A Otto von Bismarck

   B George Clemenceau

   C Archduke Franz Ferdinand

   D Kaiser Wilhelm II

5 What did Russia, a largely Slavic nation, do after Austria-Hungary declared war on the Slavic nation of Serbia?

   A declare war on Germany

   B pledge to remain neutral

   C prepare to send troops to support Serbia

   D try to negotiate a settlement

_____

"Serbia must learn to fear us again."

_____

6 The quotation, was spoken to the U.S. president in 1914, after the Austrian archduke was assassinated by a Serbian student. The quotation was spoken by a diplomat from

   A France.

   B Austria-Hungary.

   C Italy.

   D Great Britain.

Name _____ Date _____

A War on Two Fronts

Specific Objective: Examine the principal theaters of battle, major turning points, and the importance of geographic factors in military decisions and outcomes.

Read the summaries to answer questions on the next page.

During World War I, the **Central Powers** (Austria-Hungary, Germany, the Ottoman Turks, and Bulgaria) faced enemies on both sides of their borders—France to the west, and Russia to the east. France, Russia, Great Britain, and Italy in 1915 were the **Allied Powers**. Fighting concentrated in these border areas, which became known as the **Western Front** and the **Eastern Front**. Germany's strategy, the **Schlieffen Plan**, was first to attack France through neutral Belgium, before Russia on the Eastern Front had a chance to gather its forces.

The Western Front

• After initial gains by the Germans, French and British troops were victorious at the **First Battle of the Marne** (September 1914). Germany realized that victory on the Western Front would not be quick and changed its strategy.

• Combat on the Western Front was marked by bloodshed and stalemate largely because of **trench warfare**, in which soldiers fought each other from deep, rat-infested trenches. By early 1915, 600 miles of trenches stretched from the English Channel to the Swiss Border. Soldiers lived in horrible conditions and faced threats from efficient modern weapons and poison gas.

• The **Battle of Verdun** and the **Battle of the Somme** each raged for months during 1916, and the **Battles of Ypres** took place between 1914 and 1918. Little ground was gained in these conflicts, but the human toll was staggering—each battle yielded more than 1 million casualties.

The Eastern Front

• Russia and the Serbs battled the Central Powers on the Eastern Front. There, Germany won a number of victories. At the **Battle of Tannenberg** (1914), Germany won a decisive victory over Russia. In 1915, the Central Powers continued to sweep through Russia and claimed victory in Poland; in 1916 they claimed victory in Romania.

• Russia was old-fashioned country fighting a modern war. Russian soldiers faced the well-armed Germans with little more than courage. The Russians had only one asset—numbers. For more than three years, the enormous Russian army tied up the German army in the East. Thus, Germany could never hurl its full fighting force on the West.

Name _____ Date _____

PRACTICE

A War on Two Fronts

Directions: Choose the letter of the *best* answer.

1 **Why did Germany have a geographic disadvantage at the start of World War I?**

 A It was a landlocked nation.

 B It was bordered by enemies on two fronts.

 C Its inland mountain ranges were nearly impassable.

 D Its major rivers blocked the movement of troops.

2 **Germany's Schlieffen Plan for military attack was to**

 A first attack Russia with lightening speed before facing France in the West.

 B attack France in the West before Russia in the East had a chance to mobilize.

 C try to get the United States to align itself with Germany.

 D engage both France in the West and Russia in the East at the same time.

3 **After the Battle of the Marne in 1914, German forces realized that victory**

 A would be theirs, as long as they stuck to the plan.

 B on the Western Front would not be quick.

 C against the West could only be won through trench warfare.

 D in the East could only be achieved before the harsh Russian winter began.

4 **Trench warfare in World War I was characterized by**

 A a series of Russian victories.

 B swift invasions and decisive attacks.

 C heavy casualties and little territorial gain.

 D tremendous German victories in the East.

5 **During World War I, Russia's main strength was its**

 A control of the seas.

 B industrial production.

 C large number of soldiers.

 D military technology.

6 **In November 2003, workers digging to build a highway near Ypres, Belgium, uncovered a network of shallow passages and found skeletons in World War I–era uniforms, newspapers, dishes and other items. The finding is most likely**

 A an unmarked World War I grave along the Eastern Front.

 B a World War I hiding place for civilians.

 C a bunk site for World War I troops.

 D a site of trench warfare.

Name _____   Date _____

**CALIFORNIA CONTENT
STANDARD 10.5.3**

Major Events Affecting the Course of World War I

Specific Objective: Explain how the Russian Revolution and the entry of the United States affected the course and outcome of the war.

Read the sequence charts to answer questions on the next page.

The Turning Point of the War

The war dragged on. Hundreds of thousands of people had died or were homeless. Every country was short of food and weapons. Then, in 1917, a series of events brought the war to an end. The first event took place in Russia.

The Russian Revolution

Revolution Begins: In February, 1917, the women of St. Petersburg went out to buy food. When they discovered that shops were empty, they gathered in the streets. Others joined them, and a riot began. The tsar sent in troops, but the soldiers joined the rioters. A few days later, the tsar gave up. Russia no longer had a ruler.

↓

Temporary Government: With the tsar gone, a temporary government took over to fight the war. In several cities, soldiers and workers formed soviets, or councils. These groups challenged the new government, especially its desire to keep fighting.

↓

Lenin: In October 1917, a radical group known as the Bolsheviks took over, led by Vladimir Lenin. He called for the soviets to take over the government.

↓

Surrender: On November 7, 1917, the Bolsheviks took over the country. By spring 1918, Russia and Germany had signed the Treaty of Brest-Litovsk. Germany and Austria no longer had to fight in the East. They could send more troops to fight on the Western Front.

The United States Enters World War I

U.S. Neutrality: For many years, the United States had stayed neutral. However, in 1917, the Germans announced unrestricted submarine warfare. Their submarines would sink, without warning, any ship in the waters around Britain.

↓

A New War: German U-boats sank three U.S. ships bound for Great Britain. On April 2, 1917, the U.S. entered the war on the side of the Allies.

↓

To the Rescue: By June of 1918, U.S. troops were arriving in France at the rate of 250,000 a month. The U.S. also provided tons of food and about $10 billion in loans to the Allied governments.

↓

Ambiens: By 1918, German troops were exhausted. The Americans were numerous and eager to fight. In August, the decisive battle of the war took place near Ambiens, France. About 300 Allied tanks broke the German lines.

↓

The End of the War: The Germans' resources were strained. The Central Powers were crumbling. On November 9, the German Kaiser gave up his throne. On November 11, a new German republic signed an agreement ending the war.

PRACTICE

CALIFORNIA CONTENT STANDARD 10.5.3

Major Events Affecting the Course of World War I

Directions: Choose the letter of the *best* answer.

1 **What was the immediate goal of Lenin and the Bolsheviks?**

A to gain access to Germany's industrial resources

B to help the temporary government fight the war

C to end Russia's involvement in the war

D to return the tsar to power

2 **What happened when the Treaty of Brest-Litovsk was signed?**

A The Russians pulled out of the war.

B The treaty ended World War I

C Germany withdrew from the war.

D The United States entered the war.

3 **Which German action was *most* important in bringing the United States into World War I?**

A German invasion of Russia

B unrestricted submarine warfare

C trench warfare on the Western Front

D German use of poison gas

4 **By the time the United States entered World War I, fighting was focused on**

A the Eastern Front

B the Western Front

C former Russian territory

D the seas around Great Britain

5 **After entering World War I, the United States *most* helped the Allies by**

A fighting Germany in the sea around Britain.

B negotiating with the Central Powers.

C sending the Allies supplies, troops, and monetary loans.

D trying to convince the Russians to return to fighting.

6 **What *main* motivation finally forced the Central Powers to surrender on November 11, 1918?**

A They did not have the resources or soldiers to fight the Americans.

B Their people refused to fight any longer.

C Austria-Hungary had already signed a peace treaty with the Allies.

D They no longer wanted to fight the large Russian army in the East.

Name _____ Date _____

The Human Costs of World War I

Specific Objective: Understand the nature of the war and its human costs on all sides of the conflict, including how colonial peoples contributed to the war effort.

Read the summaries and the chart to answer questions on the next page.

The War to End All Wars World War I was called "the war to end all wars." The destruction it caused was so extreme, people could not bear the thought of another war.

Military Casualties In the first three years, Europe lost more lives than it had in three hundred years of war before that. Deadly new weapons, such as the machine gun and the submarine, along with infection killed an estimated 8.5 million soldiers. About 21 million more were wounded. Trench warfare led to daily deaths from artillery. Poison gas caused many deaths and serious injuries.

	Total Mobilized Forces	Killed or Died[1]	Wounded	Prisoners or Missing	Total Casualties	Casualty Rate
Central Powers*	22,850,000	3,386,200	8,388,448	3,629,829	15,404,477	67.4%
Allies**	42,188,810	5,142,631	12,800,706	4,121,090	22,064,427	52.3%

* Germany, Austria-Hungary, Bulgaria, and Turkey
** 95% of troops were from Russia, the British Empire, France, Italy, the United States, and Japan.
1. Includes death from all causes.   Source: U.S. Department of Defense

Effects on Civilians

• The countries involved in World War I focused their total efforts on winning. Civilians worked to produce war-related materials. Many goods, especially food and fuel, were rationed.

• Millions of civilians died from disease, starvation, and bombing and fighting on their own lands. The war destroyed their homes, farms, and towns.

• The flu epidemic of 1918 traveled around the world, wherever soldiers fought. It killed more people than the war itself.

• The Russian Revolution continued after the war ended. It resulted in millions of civilian deaths. Massacres were another source of high civilian casualties.

Colonial Participation One reason a European war, became a "World War" was the participation of colonial peoples. Great Britain used soldiers from India, Kenya, Nigeria, South Africa, and others. French colonies in West Africa, and German colonies in East Africa sent troops. Allied forces attacked German colonies in China, the Pacific islands, and Africa. Although some individuals defended their ruling countries eagerly, others fought because they were required to serve. After the war, those who survived returned home to find that, as colonial subjects, they were still second-class citizens.

PRACTICE

CALIFORNIA CONTENT
STANDARD 10.5.4

The Human Costs of World War I

Directions: Choose the letter of the *best* answer.

Use the chart on page 61 to answer questions 1 and 2.

1 What conclusion can be drawn from these data about casualties in World War I?

A The Central Powers had more total casualties than the Allies.

B Most of the casualties were prisoners or missing.

C The Allies had a lower casualty rate than the Central Powers.

D The number killed was greater than the number wounded.

2 Which reason for Allied victory is supported by the chart?

A fewer wounded soldiers

B greater number of troops

C deadliest weapons

D took more prisoners

3 What is *one* reason why millions of European and Russian civilians died during World War I?

A They were not as strong as civilians during other wars.

B They did not hide from the enemy.

C The Allied troops ignored their plight

D Much of the fighting took place in Europe and Russia.

4 Civilian casualties in World War I were

A fewer than military casualties.

B extremely rare.

C increased by disease and starvation.

D primarily due to overwork.

5 Which country recruited colonial troops from India in World War I?

A Britain

B France

C Germany

D Japan

6 After World War I, some colonies that had participated made demands for independence primarily because

A American troops taught colonists that all men are created equal.

B colonists felt entitled to citizenship because they had served in the military.

C colonists were inspired by the example of the Russian Revolution.

D colonists were afraid for their jobs in the unstable European economy.

**CALIFORNIA CONTENT
STANDARD 10.5.5**

Human Rights Violations and Genocide

Specific Objective: Discuss human rights violations and genocide during World War I, including the Ottoman government's actions against Armenian citizens.

Read the summaries to answer questions on the next page.

Atrocities on Both Sides

- The Allies accused the Germans of committing atrocities, or terrible crimes, against Belgium, a neutral nation. The British government issued a report investigating the situation. It was later shown to have overstated many of the claims. Still, the Germans admitted to using harsh measures in achieving their goals. An estimated 5,500 Belgians were killed. Many towns and buildings were destroyed or plundered. Charges of German atrocities were used as propaganda in neutral countries.

- Many Allies also pointed to other examples of Germany's inhumane tactics. These included the use of poison gas and the sinking of passenger ships such as the American *Lusitania*. Yet the Allies themselves soon started using poison gas. The *Lusitania* was carrying weapons as well as passengers.

- The Allies blocked trade with Germany for five years. This blockade caused great suffering for the German people. German government records show that 763,000 people starved to death as a result of this Allied action.

The Armenian Genocide

- The Armenians were an ethnic minority of about 2.5 million in the Ottoman Empire ruled by Turkey. As Christians in a mainly Muslim land, they were also a religious minority. They had long been denied basic rights and wanted to be independent. When war broke out, they pledged to support the Allies, the enemies of the Turks.

- Just before the war began, a group of extreme nationalists took over the Turkish government. They vowed to create a Turkish-only state. On April 24, 1915, the government began forcing Armenians from their homes. Some Armenians were killed outright. Many others, sent on forced marches to the Syrian Desert, died of starvation or disease. Virtually all who survived were left homeless. The persecution continued from 1915 to 1918 and arose again from 1920 to 1923. At least 600,000 Armenians died between 1915 and 1916 alone.

- The murder and planned murder of an entire group of people, especially an ethnic group, is called genocide.

- Many foreigners in the Ottoman Empire witnessed this destruction of the Armenian population. They told the outside world of the horrors they had seen. The international community officially condemned the genocide. Yet they made no forceful effort to save the Armenians.

Name _____   Date _____

PRACTICE

CALIFORNIA CONTENT
STANDARD 10.5.5

*Human Rights Violations
and Genocide*

Directions: Choose the letter of the *best* answer.

1 Stories of German atrocities in
Belgium were used as propaganda,
meaning that the stories were
used to

 A encourage Belgium to support the
war.

 B make the Germans look worse than
they were.

 C convince neutral nations to fight for
the German army.

 D show that the Germans treated
civilians humanely.

2 Which statement *best* describes the
existence of atrocities during World
War I?

 A Both sides followed the rules of
warfare and avoided civilian deaths.

 B Germany was the only member of the
Central Powers that killed civilians.

 C The Allies were fighting for
democracy and did not harm civilians.

 D Both sides justified the use of harsh
tactics to achieve their military goals.

3 The Armenians in Turkey were a
minority group partly because they
were

 A atheist.

 B Christian.

 C Jewish.

 D Muslim.

4 The Ottoman Empire was ruled by

 A the Armenians.

 B the Germans.

 C the Turks.

 D a European coalition.

5 What was the political position of
the Armenians at the beginning of
World War I?

 A They supported the Turks.

 B They supported the Allies.

 C They wished to remain neutral.

 D Their position was unknown.

6 How did the international
community respond to Turkey's
actions against the Armenians?

 A It supported the Turkish
government's actions.

 B It tried to keep Turkey's actions
secret until after the war.

 C It did not know about the actions
until after the war.

 D It condemned Turkey but did not fight
to save the Armenians.

Name _____ Date _____

**CALIFORNIA CONTENT
STANDARD 10.6.1**   *The Treaty of Versailles*

Specific Objective: Analyze the aims and roles of world leaders in negotiating the terms of the Treaty of Versailles; Analyze the influence of Woodrow Wilson's Fourteen Points; Analyze the causes and effects of U.S. rejection of the League of Nations.

Read the summaries to answer questions on the next page.

The Fourteen Points

During World War I, U.S. President Woodrow Wilson drew up a proposal for postwar peace that was known as the Fourteen Points. It included:

- general suggestions for **encouraging peace**, such as an **end to secret treaties**
- specific recommendations for changing borders and creating new nations, based on the principle of national **self-determination**—allowing people to decide for themselves under what government they wished to live
- a call for "a general association of nations" that would peacefully negotiate solutions to world conflicts, Wilson's **Fourteenth Point**, which led to the creation of the **League of Nations**

Negotiating the Treaty of Versailles

The Fourteen Points were the basis for talks that led to the 1919 Treaty of Versailles.

- The talks were attended by delegates from Allied and neutral nations.
- Germany and its allies were not allowed to participate.
- Most negotiations were made by the so-called **Big Four**: **George Clemenceau**, premier of France—wanted Germany to be punished; **Vittorio Emanuele Orlando**, premier of Italy—sought territory for Italy; **David Lloyd George**, prime minister of Great Britain—worked for compromise; **Woodrow Wilson**, U.S. president—had to abandon many of his Fourteen Points.

Terms of the Treaty

- The League of Nations, an international peace organization, is established; Germany and Russia are excluded from membership.
- Germany returns the provinces of Alsace and Lorraine to France, gives up its overseas colonies, reduces its army in size, is forbidden to buy or make weapons, and to have submarines or an air force, is assigned sole responsibility for the war, and must pay the Allies $33 billion in wartime reparations.

The United States Rejects the League of Nations

In November 1919, the U.S. Senate rejected the Treaty of Versailles. The League of Nations was the main sticking point. Some Americans were concerned that membership in the League would diminish the right of the United States to make its own decisions. More importantly, the treaty required each member nation to support the boundaries of other member nations—a requirement that many feared could lead to U.S. involvement in future European wars.

Copyright © McDougal Littell/Houghton Mifflin Company

CSS Specific Objective 10.6.1: Review **65**

Name _____ Date _____

CALIFORNIA CONTENT
STANDARD 10.6.1

The Treaty of Versailles

Directions: Choose the letter of the *best* answer.

1 U.S. president Woodrow Wilson's Fourteen Points were

  A the basis for determining German reparations.

  B a charter for the League of Nations.

  C an outcome of the Treaty of Versailles.

  D a plan for postwar peace.

2 Which statement *best* summarizes the idea of national self-determination as it was presented in Woodrow Wilson's Fourteen Points?

  A Strong national boundaries strengthen national unity.

  B Voter participation in a democracy is the best way to encourage peace.

  C All people have the right to independence from colonial rule.

  D People should be able to decide on their type of government.

3 The Big Four who negotiated the Treaty of Versailles represented France, Great Britain, the United States, and what other nation?

  A Germany

  B Italy

  C Russia

  D Spain

4 Which of the following did the Treaty of Versailles require of Germany?

  A payment of damages to its overseas colonies

  B a public apology to the Allies

  C acceptance of sole responsibility for the war

  D division into two states: West Germany and East Germany

5 The *main* purpose of the League of Nations was to

  A keep the peace and prevent future wars.

  B regulate commercial and economic competition.

  C impose sanctions on aggressive nations.

  D achieve international cooperation in governing colonies.

6 What is the *main* reason that Americans rejected the League of Nations?

  A They objected to Germany's membership.

  B They believed the financial aid it provided would burden the U.S. economy.

  C They feared it could lead to future U.S. involvement in European wars.

  D They did not want to help rebuild postwar Europe.

Name _____ Date _____

Europe After World War I

Specific Objective: Describe the effects of World War I and resulting terms of peace on population shifts, world economy, and political borders in Europe and the Middle East.

Read the maps and the summary to answer questions on the next page.

The Treaty of Versailles was only one of a number of treaties negotiated at the end of World War I. The treaties resulted in new national boundaries and new countries.

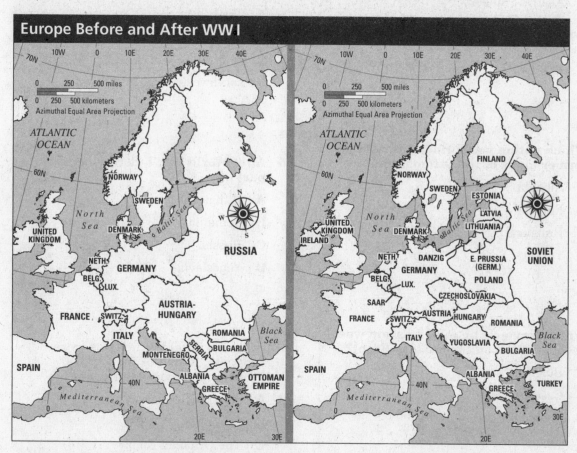

Europe Before and After WW I

As the maps show, the postwar treaties carved up old empires into many small new nations, causing huge land losses for the Central Powers and changing the face of Europe.

- The former empire of Austria-Hungary was dissolved, and new nations were created from its land: Austria, Hungary, Czechoslovakia, and Yugoslavia.

- The Ottoman Turks had to give up much of their land in southwest Asia and the Middle East. In Europe, they retained only the country of Turkey.

- Poland, which had long been divided among Germany, Russia, and Austria-Hungary, was reconstituted.

- Russian land yielded the new nations of Finland, Estonia, Latvia, and Lithuania.

- Russia and Austria-Hungary gave up additional territory to Poland and Romania.

PRACTICE

CALIFORNIA CONTENT
STANDARD 10.6.2

Europe After World War I

Directions: Choose the letter of the *best* answer.

Use the maps on page 67 to answer questions 1–6.

1 Who lost the *greatest* percentage of land in the creation of new nations?

A Austria-Hungary

B France

C Germany

D Russia

2 Which nation was formed from the former lands of the Ottoman Empire?

A Albania

B Finland

C Hungary

D Turkey

3 Which formerly dissolved nation was reconstituted on the Eastern Front?

A Bulgaria

B Czechoslovakia

C Poland

D Romania

4 In what region of Europe were the new nations of Finland, Estonia, Latvia, and Lithuania created?

A northeast

B northwest

C southeast

D southwest

5 After World War I, Serbia became part of

A Hungary.

B Romania.

C Russia.

D Yugoslavia.

6 After national boundaries were redrawn, which of the Central Powers lost access to the sea?

A Austria-Hungary

B Germany

C The Ottoman Empire

D Russia

Name _____ Date _____

CALIFORNIA CONTENT
STANDARD 10.6.3

Postwar Disillusionment in Europe

Specific Objective: Understand the widespread disillusionment with prewar institutions, authorities, and values that resulted in a void that was later filled by totalitarians.

Read the summary and cluster diagram to answer questions on the next page.

World War I shook the economic and political foundations of Europe. The war left nearly every major nation bankrupt and, after centuries of rule by kings, brought an end to the continent's last great empires.

The diagram shows some of the troubles facing postwar Europe. In several countries, these troubles paved the way for the rise of **totalitarian** government—a government which takes total control over nearly every aspect of people's lives.

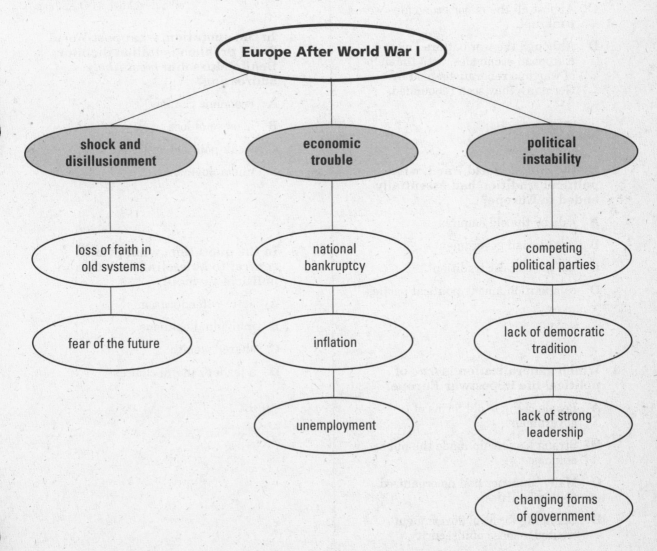

Name _____ Date _____

PRACTICE

CALIFORNIA CONTENT
STANDARD 10.6.3

*Postwar Disillusionment
in Europe*

Directions: Choose the letter of the *best* answer.

1 Which statement *best* describes national economies in Europe after World War I?

  A In most areas, wartime industry brought significant economic gains.

  B Western Europe remained economically strong, but the economies of eastern and southern Europe were devastated.

  C Almost all the major economies were bankrupt.

  D Although the war battered most European economies, with the help of wartime reparations paid by Germany, they soon rebounded.

2 By the end of World War I, what political tradition had essentially ended in Europe?

  A rule by the old empires

  B totalitarian government

  C the democratic tradition

  D competition among political parties

3 Which generalization is *true* of political life in postwar Europe?

  A People clung to old forms of government.

  B Strong leadership made the public anxious.

  C Many countries had no organized political parties.

  D Changing forms of government created a sense of insecurity.

Use the quotation to answer questions 4 and 5.

"It is the State which educates its citizens in civic virtue, gives them a consciousness of their mission, and welds them into unity."

—Benito Mussolini, from *The Social and Political Doctrines of Contemporary Europe,* edited by Michael Oakeshott

4 In the quotation, what post-World War I problem is Italian dictator Benito Mussolini *most likely* addressing?

  A economic change

  B a sense of loss

  C weak political systems

  D unemployment

5 In the quotation, what is most central to Mussolini's solution to political turmoil?

  A state-run education

  B individual opinions

  C shared wealth

  D a leader's moral choices

Name _____ Date _____

Artists in the West After World War I

Specific Objective: Discuss the influence of World War I on literature, art, and intellectual life in the West (e.g., Pablo Picasso, the "lost generation" of writers).

Read the summary and the chart to answer questions on the next page.

The years after World War I brought an outpouring of creative work. Many artists and thinkers felt cynical about the past, and sought new means of expressing themselves. Some composers experimented with harsh combinations of sounds; some painters explored the idea that things are not what they seem. Many of these means of expression had emerged around the turn of the century, but the war accelerated their development.

The term **"lost generation"** describes a group of **American writers in Paris** after the war, including **Ernest Hemingway, F. Scott Fitzgerald,** and **Gertrude Stein.** Their writing sometimes conveyed a sense of loss and meaninglessness. The term "lost generation" is also used in a general way to describe those who grew up during the war, saw the old ideals fail, and had to work to find new meaning in an unstable world.

Art	
Rebelled *against* . . .	• *realistic styles, traditional compositions*
Explored . . .	• world of dreams and fantasy • seeing shapes in new ways
Famous Figures	• Pablo Picasso (Spain) • René Magritte (France)

Architecture	
Rebelled *against* . . .	• *grand structures designed for old empires*
Explored . . .	• machine-age materials (glass, steel, concrete) • efficient and cost-effective design
Famous Figures	• Le Corbusier (France) • Walter Gropius (Germany)

Literature	
Rebelled *against* . . .	• *romantic idealism, easy solutions*
Explored . . .	• feelings of loss and fear • new ways of using old literary forms
Famous Figures	• James Joyce (Ireland) • Ernest Hemingway (United States)

Music	
Rebelled *against* . . .	*regular rhythms, traditional compositions*
Explored . . .	• irregular rhythms • improvisational and dissonant forms
Famous Figures	• Igor Stravinsky (Russian) • American jazz musicians

Name _____   Date _____

PRACTICE

CALIFORNIA CONTENT
STANDARD 10.6.4

*Artists in the West
After World War I*

Directions: Choose the letter of the *best* answer.

Use the quotation to answer questions 1 and 2.

In the post-World War I novel, *All Quiet on the Western Front*, a young soldier named Paul says of the older generation:

"The idea of authority, which they represented, was associated in our minds with a greater insight and a more humane wisdom. But the first death we saw shattered this belief."

—from *All Quiet on the Western Front*,
Erich Maria Remarque

1   What common post-World War I literary theme is characterized by Paul in the quotation from *All Quiet on the Western Front*?

   A   Poor military leadership had created a war that could not be won.

   B   Young soldiers were lured to die in battle under false pretenses.

   C   The horrors of war destroyed the young soldiers' trust in their elders.

   D   Life on the battlefield meant that soldiers rarely saw their leaders.

2   Which emotion *best* describes *both* Paul's words in the quotation, and "lost generation" literature in general?

   A   patriotism

   B   terror

   C   relief

   D   disillusionment

3   After World War I, many artists, architects, writers, and musicians rejected

   A   government funding.

   B   traditional styles.

   C   cultural change.

   D   their own feelings.

4   What project would *likely* be chosen by a European architect, such as Le Corbusier or Gropius, after World War I?

   A   a luxury apartment building decorated with carved limestone

   B   a splendid monument honoring the new state leadership

   C   a space-efficient dormitory built of steel and glass

   D   the restoration of a palace that was damaged in the war

5   The "lost generation" of writers who gathered in Paris were considered "lost" because

   A   the war had left them with a sense of meaninglessness.

   B   they wrote about soldiers who were unable to return home.

   C   their homes were destroyed in the war.

   D   shifting boundaries meant they no longer lived in their nations of origin.

Name _____ Date _____

Causes and Consequences of the Russian Revolution

Specific Objective: Understand the causes and consequences of the Russian Revolution, including Lenin's use of totalitarian means to seize and maintain control.

Read the summaries to answer questions on the next page.

The Russian Revolution

The Russian Revolution is dated to November 1917 (October 1917 on the Russian calendar), when Bolshevik Party forces took over the government offices in Petrograd. However, the problems that led toward revolution had been developing for generations. The revolution's consequences, too, were far-reaching—the Communist Party, which formed to lead post-revolutionary Russia, remained in power until 1991.

Causes

- Widespread suffering under **autocracy**—a form of government in which one person, in this case the czar, has absolute power
- Weak leadership of **Czar Nicholas II**—clung to autocracy despite changing times
- Poor working conditions, low wages, and hazards of industrialization
- New revolutionary movements that believed a worker-run government should replace czarist rule
- Russian defeat in the Russo-Japanese War (1905), which led to rising unrest
- **Bloody Sunday**, the massacre of unarmed protestors outside the palace, in 1905
- Devastation of World War I—high casualties, economic ruin, widespread hunger
- The **March Revolution** in 1917, in which soldiers who were brought in for crowd control ultimately joined labor activists in calling "Down with the autocracy!"

Consequences

- The government is taken over by the **Bolshevik Party**, led by **V. I. Lenin**; later, it will be known as the Communist Party.
- Farmland is distributed among farmers, and factories are given to workers.
- Banks are nationalized and a national council is assembled to run the economy.
- Russia pulls out of World War I, signing the Treaty of Brest-Litovsk, conceding much land to Germany.
- Czarist rule ends. Nicholas II, his wife and five children are executed.
- Civil war, between Bolshevik ("red") and anti-Bolshevik ("white") forces, sweeps Russia from 1918 to 1920. Around 15 million die in conflict and the famine
- The Russian economy is in shambles. Industrial production drops, trade all but ceases, and skilled workers flee the country.
- Lenin asserts his control by cruel methods such as the **Gulag**, a vast and brutal network of prison camps for both criminals and political prisoners.

Name _____ Date _____

Causes and Consequences of the Russian Revolution

Directions: Choose the letter of the *best* answer.

1 *One* **factor that led to the Russian Revolution was**

  A problems associated with industrialization.

  B civil war between "red" and "white" forces.

  C nationalization of the banking industry.

  D the Treaty of Brest-Litovsk.

2 **Who was the leader of the Bolsheviks?**

  A Nicholas II

  B Karl Marx

  C V. I. Lenin

  D Joseph Stalin

3 **After the Russian Revolution, the czar and his family were**

  A exiled to Siberia.

  B executed by revolutionaries.

  C figureheads—political figures with no actual power.

  D advisers to Russia's first parliament.

4 **The Gulag was a network of**

  A labor activists.

  B revolutionaries.

  C prison camps.

  D worker-owned factories.

5 **Which event was a *direct* result of the Russian Revolution?**

  A The Russian economy rebounded.

  B Factory workers began to demand their rights.

  C Russia was defeated in the Russo-Japanese War.

  D Russia pulled out of World War I.

6 **Which statement *best* describes conditions surrounding the March Revolution of 1917?**

  A Lenin was concerned about competition from other revolutionaries.

  B Support for revolutionary activity was increasing.

  C Peace with Germany was considered more important than keeping territory.

  D The czar would stop at nothing to protect the autocracy.

Name _____ Date _____

REVIEW

CALIFORNIA CONTENT
STANDARD 10.7.2

Stalinist Russia

Specific Objective: Trace Stalin's rise to power in the Soviet Union; trace the connection between economic and political policies, absence of a free press, and systematic violations of human rights.

Read the summaries to answer questions on the next page.

After the death of V. I. Lenin, Joseph Stalin took control of the Communist Party in Russia. While Lenin had wanted to unite the workers of the world, Stalin focused on transforming Russia into a **totalitarian** state. In a totalitarian state, a government takes near total control over people's daily lives. Stalin and party leaders used violence to assert their totalitarian power.

Economic Control: Stalin's government made all economic decisions in a system that was known as **command economy**. Economic control included:
- Setting goals for rapid industrial growth
- Choosing workers and setting their wages
- Telling workers where they could live
- Organizing collective farms, to produce food for the state

Political Control: Stalin held absolute power, outlawed all other political parties, and demanded obedience, which was enforced in part by secret police (and a system of **police terror** that treated ordinary citizens like criminals). Government control included:
- Using tanks and weapons to stop protests
- Tapping telephone lines and reading mail
- Jailing and executing political opponents
- Asserting the right to punish any person for disobedience—almost any act

Cultural Control: Under Stalin, the government used means of mass communication to shape people's thinking toward absolute faith in the Communist Party, including
- Controlling all newspapers, radio stations, and movie studios
- Destroying churches and synagogues and killing or imprisoning religious leaders
- Controlling all education, including curriculum, textbooks, and teaching
- Censoring many writers, painters, and composers, and forced others to create **propaganda**—biased or false information used to influence people

Reign of Terror: Under Stalin, Russians lost most basic rights. Millions died—an estimated 8 to 13 million. In the Ukraine, an area that resisted rule by Stalin, his government confiscated food, forcing an estimated 5 million people to starve. The event is the **Terror Famine**.

Copyright © McDougal Littell/Houghton Mifflin Company

Name _____ Date _____

PRACTICE

Stalinist Russia

_____

Directions: Choose the letter of the *best* answer.

1 What is *one key* trait of a totalitarian system of government?

   A worker control of industry

   B the use of violence

   C freedom of the press

   D multi-party rule

4 In Stalinist Russia, religious leaders were

   A forced to create propaganda.

   B mostly ignored.

   C often persecuted.

   D helpful in keeping people obedient.

2 In Stalin's command economy,

   A workers set their own hours.

   B the government alone made all decisions.

   C millions returned to subsistence farming.

   D migrant labor became a major force.

5 What was *one* goal of the Communist government of Stalin's Soviet Union when they tapped people's telephones and read their mail?

   A pioneering new technologies

   B looking for a worthy new leader

   C increasing open communication

   D making people afraid to protest

3 Police terror was a weapon used by Joseph Stalin, *mainly* against

   A Communist leaders.

   B ordinary Russians.

   C Ukrainians.

   D the military.

6 What caused 5 million Ukrainians to starve under Stalin's rule?

   A their crops were destroyed by blight

   B they could not keep pace with industrialization

   C the government took their food from them

   D severe overpopulation resulted in famine

Name _____ Date _____

REVIEW

CALIFORNIA CONTENT STANDARD 10.7.3

Totalitarian Regimes in Germany, Italy, and the Soviet Union

Specific Objective: Analyze the rise, aggression, and human costs of totalitarian regimes in Germany, Italy, and the Soviet Union, noting their common and dissimilar traits.

Read the summaries and chart to answer questions on the next page.

In the years after World War I, Germany, Italy, and the Soviet Union saw the rise of **totalitarian** regimes—a form of government in which the state attempts to assert control over every aspect of public and private life. In all three countries, a new charismatic leader would become infamous for cruelty. Each of these leaders rose to power in the chaos that followed World War I, promising strength and stability to war-ravaged nations.

Nation	Germany	Italy	Soviet Union
Leader	Adolf Hitler	Benito Mussolini	Joseph Stalin
Political Party	Nazi (National Socialists)	Fascist	Communist
Dates In Power	1933–1945	1922–1945	1928–1953
Unifying Idea	Germans as "master race"	strongly nationalistic	desire for a classless society
Economic Policy	capitalist; government/ business partnerships	capitalist; government/ business partnerships	communist; state owns everything, controls economy
Control of Media	total	less than total	total
Religious Control	some freedom, but not for Jews	Catholicism was state religion; free choice	religion suppressed
Use of Terror	Millions killed; Jews and Romani particularly, and many non-Germans, and minorities were singled out for terror.	murder rare; about 4,000 imprisoned	secret police imprisoned and killed over 20 million.

The totalitarian regimes shared a number of **similarities**, including:

• Ruled by a dictator who was glorified as a hero
• Allowed only one political party
• Emphasized total loyalty to the government and its leader
• Denied individual rights
• Censored the press and other media
• Used art, culture, and mass communications to spread propaganda
• Encouraged a high birthrate; rewarded women who had many children
• Controlled people by terror, especially by means of secret police
• As police states, used secret police to terrorize people.

PRACTICE

CALIFORNIA CONTENT
STANDARD 10.7.3

Totalitarian Regimes in Germany, Italy, and the Soviet Union

Directions: Choose the letter of the *best* answer.

1 **What conditions surrounded the rise of totalitarianism in Germany, Italy, and the Soviet Union?**

  A Each totalitarian regime arose after a revolution.

  B All the regimes re-energized weak capitalist systems.

  C The regimes followed the devastation of World War I.

  D Each regime, built upon a former totalitarian government.

2 **Which traits were shared by *all* three regimes—Germany, Italy, and the Soviet Union—during the 1930s?**

  A single-party rule

  B widespread use of murder

  C total control of the media

  D state control of the economy

3 **Which trait was *unique* to the totalitarian regime in Germany compared with other totalitarian governments of the 1930s?**

  A encouragement of a high birth rate

  B Catholicism as a state religion

  C an emphasis on total obedience to the leader

  D belief in a "master race"

4 **Which trait was *unique* to the totalitarian regime in the Soviet Union compared with other regimes of the 1930s?**

  A religious freedom

  B partnerships between government and businesses

  C a desire for a classless society

  D the widespread use of propaganda

5 **A *main* reason that an estimated 20 million Soviet citizens were imprisoned under Stalin was that they were**

  A at war with the government.

  B Jewish.

  C not really citizens.

  D suspected of opposing Stalin.

6 **In a police state, the police carry out the will of**

  A police chiefs.

  B the ruling leader.

  C the people.

  D military equals.

Name _____ Date _____

The Drive for Empire in Germany, Italy, and Japan

Specific Objective: Compare the German, Italian, and Japanese drives for empire in the 1930s, including the 1937 Rape of Nanking, other atrocities in China, and the Hitler-Stalin pact of 1939.

Read the summary to answer questions on the next page.

After World War I, Italy, Japan, and Germany all sought to increase their might. Italy and Germany still suffered the effects of the war, and Japan wanted to further the power it had gained during wartime.

By the 1930s, all three were led by military dictatorships in which the state held tremendous power and sought to expand that power by invading neighbor nations.

Italy

Led by: Benito Mussolini

Sought: a "New Roman Empire" of colonial land

Conquests: Ethiopia in 1935; Albania in 1939

- After about seven months of warfare, Italy claimed Ethiopia as its colony.

Japan

Led by: a series of military leaders, with Emperor Hirohito as a figurehead

Sought: natural resources, new markets for its goods, and room for population growth

Conquests: Manchuria, a Chinese province, in 1931; China in 1937

- From December 1937 to March 1938, Japanese troops massacred an estimated 350,000 Chinese civilians in what became known as the Rape of Nanking.
- During the Japanese occupation, millions of Chinese were killed and tens of millions became homeless.

Germany

Led by: Adolf Hitler

Sought: to rebuild its army and assert its strength

Conquests: the Rhineland (between Germany and France) in 1936; Austria in 1938; the Sudetenland area of Czechoslovakia in 1938; Czechoslovakia in 1939

- To the west, France and Britain, desiring peace at any cost, did not at first try to stop German aggression.
- To the east, Russia posed no threat after the **Hitler-Stalin Pact of 1939**, in which Germany and Russia agreed never to attack one another.

PRACTICE

CALIFORNIA CONTENT
STANDARD 10.8.1

The Drive for Empire in Germany, Italy, and Japan

Directions: Choose the letter of the *best* answer.

1 The German, Italian, and Japanese drive to empire during the 1930s had roots in

  A competition for African colonies.

  B economic expansionism.

  C tensions between communism and capitalism.

  D World War I.

2 What form of government dominated Germany, Italy, and Japan in the 1930s?

  A representative democracy

  B military dictatorship

  C military occupation

  D monarchy

3 What was Mussolini's *main* goal in the 1930s?

  A a powerful Italian army

  B a "new Roman Empire"

  C more natural resources

  D room for population growth

4 Which country did Hitler claim for Germany in 1938?

  A Austria

  B France

  C Poland

  D Yugoslavia

5 Which invasion in the late 1930s was followed by the mass murder of civilians?

  A German invasion of the Rhineland

  B German invasion of Czechoslovakia

  C Italian invasion of Ethiopia

  D Japanese invasion of China

6 What impact did the Hitler-Stalin Pact have on Germany?

  A It protected Germany from attack from the east.

  B It allowed Germany to annex Austria.

  C Germany was permitted to expand its eastern borders.

  D Germany gained access to important Soviet resources.

Name _____ Date _____

The United States and Europe Before World War II

Specific Objective: Understand the role of appeasement, nonintervention (isolationism), and domestic troubles in Europe and the United States prior to World War II.

Read the graphic organizer to answer questions on the next page.

Conditions in Europe and the United States in the 1930s
• Great Britain, France, and the United States are suffering severe economic depressions.
• Great Britain and France, remembering World War I, are determined to keep the peace.
• Germany and Italy, seeking power, move to conquer other nations.

German and Italian Aggression
1935 Italy invades Ethiopia.
1936 Germany invades the Rhineland, an area between France and Germany.
1938 Germany annexes Austria and claims the Sudetenland area of Czechoslovakia.

British, French, and U.S. Reaction
Appeasement—giving in to a potential enemy in order to keep the peace
• Great Britain and France, trying to preserve the peace, do not move to stop German and Italian aggression.
• At the Munich Conference of 1938, Great Britain and France agree to let Germany claim the Sudetenland.
Isolationism—policy of avoiding political or economic ties to other countries
• The U.S. Congress, wishing to stay out of European affairs, passes three Neutrality Acts, beginning in 1935.

German and Italian Aggression Continue
1939 In March, Germany occupies Czechoslovakia; in April, Italy invades Albania; On September 1, Germany invades Poland; on September 3, Great Britain and France declare war on Germany, and **World War II** officially begins.

PRACTICE

CALIFORNIA CONTENT
STANDARD 10.8.2

The United States and Europe Before World War II

Directions: Choose the letter of the *best* answer.

1 In the 1930s, Great Britain and France followed a policy of appeasement toward German and Italian aggression because they

   A did not want to be involved in conflict or war.

   B believed this was the best way to control Hitler and Mussolini.

   C had governments similar to Germany and Italy.

   D had a political alliance with Germany and Italy.

2 U.S. isolationists in the 1930s wished to avoid

   A political ties.

   B foreign aid.

   C economic dependence.

   D association with Nazis.

3 At the Munich Conference of 1938, Great Britain and France agreed to let Germany have

   A Austria.

   B Ethiopia.

   C the Rhineland.

   D the Sudetenland.

4 What nation did Italy invade in 1935?

   A Austria

   B Ethiopia

   C Greece

   D Switzerland

5 *One* reason why Great Britain, France, and the United States did not respond immediately to German and Italian aggression in the 1930s is that all three were

   A distracted by leisure activities.

   B focused on domestic anti-war movements.

   C concerned about the threat of communism.

   D suffering from economic depressions.

6 World War II broke out two days after Germany invaded which country?

   A Albania

   B Czechoslovakia

   C France

   D Poland

Name _____ Date _____

CALIFORNIA CONTENT STANDARD 10.8.3

The Course of World War II

Specific Objective: Identify and locate the Allied and Axis powers on a map; Discuss turning points of the war, theaters of conflict, key strategic decisions, and resulting war conferences and political resolutions, with an emphasis on geographic factors.

Read the summary to answer questions on the next page.

World War II was fought between:

- the **Axis powers** of Germany, Italy, and Japan

  and

- the **Allied powers** of Great Britain, the Soviet Union, the United States, and other nations that came together to fight the Axis powers.

Major Turning Points in World War II

1940–1941 Germany invades Denmark, Norway, the Netherlands, Belgium, France, and much of Eastern Europe and the Soviet Union. In Europe, only Great Britain remains free of German control.

Dec. 7, 1941	Japan bombs Pearl Harbor, Hawaii; the United States enters the war.
Oct. 1942–May 1943	The Allies drive the Axis powers out of North Africa.
Feb. 1943	German forces, weakened by winter Battle of Stalingrad, surrender to the Russians.
June 4, 1944	The Allies claim victory over Italy.
June 6, 1944	On D-Day, the Allies launch a massive land and sea attack at Normandy in northern France; by August, France and neighboring areas are free of Axis control.
Apr. 1945	Germany faces attacks from Allied forces (west) and Soviets (east).
May 7, 1945	Germany surrenders to the Allies.
Aug. 14, 1945	Japan surrenders to the Allies.

A Continent Divided

The end of World War II brought peace to Europe, but the continent was left divided. In 1945, even before the war ended, the Allied leaders met at the **Yalta Conference** to plan for dividing Germany into two halves—west and east—in order to weaken it. But the rest of Europe was left divided into (generally) democratic western nations and communist eastern nations. The boundary of this divide was called the **iron curtain**.

Name _____   Date _____

Directions: Choose the letter of the *best* answer.

1 **What was the *immediate* cause of U.S. entry into World War II?**

  A Germany invaded Poland.

  B Japan bombed Pearl Harbor.

  C Germany invaded the Netherlands.

  D Great Britain sought to mobilize the Allies against Hitler.

2 **In what order were the Axis powers defeated in World War II?**

  A Italy, Germany, Japan

  B Japan, Germany, Italy

  C Germany, Italy, Japan

  D Germany, Japan, Italy

3 **What was a *decisive* factor in the German defeat at the Battle of Stalingrad?**

  A superior Russian technology

  B United States intervention

  C Russian attack by land and sea

  D a prolonged harsh winter

4 **In April, 1945, Germany was attacked from the**

  A east and west.

  B north and south.

  C east and south.

  D north and west.

5 **Why was Germany divided into two parts following World War II?**

  A the Allies wanted to weaken it

  B to protect its ethnic minorities

  C to give the Soviet Union control of some of its natural resources

  D the Germans could not agree on whether to accept communism

6 **The term "iron curtain" refers to the division between**

  A Axis and Allied powers.

  B democratic and communist nations in Europe.

  C engaged and neutral nations in World War II.

  D the Soviet Union and eastern Europe.

Name _____   Date _____

Specific Objective: Describe the political, diplomatic, and military leaders during the war (e.g., Winston Churchill, Franklin Delano Roosevelt, Emperor Hirohito, Adolf Hitler, Benito Mussolini, Joseph Stalin, Douglas MacArthur, Dwight Eisenhower).

Read the chart to answer questions on the next page.

Leaders in World War II				
Leader	**Role**	**Alliance**	**Actions in World War II**	**After the War**
Winston Churchill	Prime Minister of Great Britain	Allies	Was among the first to speak out against the Nazis; led Britain and the Allies in the struggle against the Nazis	Was reelected prime minister in 1951
F. D. Roosevelt	President of the United States	Allies	Ordered U.S. entry into the war and the internment of 110,000 Japanese-Americans	Died just before the war ended in 1945
Emperor Hirohito	Emperor of Japan	Axis	Served mainly as a figure-head for various military leaders	Was emperor until his death in 1989
Adolf Hitler	Dictator of Germany	Axis	Started the war by invad-ing Poland in 1939; invaded lands in all directions in 1940–1941; led the Nazi party, which killed 11 million	Committed suicide in 1945
Benito Mussolini	Dictator of Italy	Axis	Formed an alliance with Germany; suffered military defeats and was overthrown by the Italian king in 1943	Killed by Italian insurgents in 1945
Joseph Stalin	Dictator of the Soviet Union	Allies	Cooperated with Germany until Germany violated the Hitler-Stalin pact by invading the Soviet Union in 1941, then joined the Allies	Was dictator until his death in 1953
Douglas MacArthur	U.S. Army General	Allies	Commanded Allied forces in the Pacific	Led U.S. troops in the Korean War
Dwight Eisenhower	U.S. Army General	Allies	Commanded Allied forces in Europe; led the D-Day invasion of mainland Europe; helped unite Allied troops	Elected U.S. president in 1952

PRACTICE

CALIFORNIA CONTENT STANDARD 10.8.4

Leaders in World War II

Directions: Choose the letter of the *best* answer.

Use the cartoon to answer questions 1–3.

Daily Mail, London, 23 June 1941. Reprinted with permission.

1 The cartoon depicts what World War II event or issue?

A Soviet trust in Nazi Germany

B Germany's war on communism

C Nazi imprisonment of Russian soldiers

D the German invasion of the Soviet Union

2 The cartoon depicts Russia and Germany by what symbols?

A two figures in national uniforms

B recognizable caricatures of Stalin and Hitler

C oil wells behind Stalin and airplanes behind Hitler

D the stereotypes of foolish and wicked faces

3 Hitler is shown simultaneously hugging and stabbing Stalin, causing Stalin to drop what document?

A the Soviet plan of attack

B the Communist Manifesto

C the Munich Agreement

D the Hitler-Stalin Pact

4 Whose stance against Hitler was *most* significant in mobilizing the Allied powers?

A Winston Churchill

B Dwight D. Eisenhower

C Douglas MacArthur

D Franklin D. Roosevelt

Name _____ Date _____

CALIFORNIA CONTENT
STANDARD 10.8.5

The Holocaust

Specific Objective: Analyze the Nazi policy of pursuing racial purity, especially against the European Jews; its transformation into the Final Solution; and the Holocaust that resulted in the murder of six million Jewish civilians.

Read the summary to answer questions on the next page.

Nazi Ideology

The Nazi party believed that people were racially unequal. In their ideology, Germanic peoples, whom they called **Aryans**, were the "master race." Other peoples were considered inferior—especially Jews. The Nazis believed that other races threatened the "purity" of the Aryan race; they wanted to increase the Aryan race and limit other races.

Nazis' beliefs about racial inequality had various implications. For example, they used it to justify their drive for **Lebensraum**—"living space," or room for their own population growth—by invading the eastern European lands of Slavic peoples, whom they deemed inferior. But the most violent Nazi ideology targeted the Jews.

Persecution of the Jews

Soon after Hitler took power in 1933, Jewish persecution began. Under Hitler, Jews were:

- stripped of citizenship and other rights under the **Nuremberg Laws** (1935)
- terrorized by attacks on their homes and businesses, such as **Kristallnacht** (1938)
- deprived of property and forced into **ghettos**—crowded, isolated areas where many died of starvation and disease (1940)

The "Final Solution"

After World War II broke out in 1939, Jewish persecution spread. In Eastern Europe, the Nazis began to send out killing squads. They also built brutal slave-labor camps.

Around 1942, the persecution became a **genocide**—an effort to kill an entire group of people. The Nazis built death camps that served as centers for the mass murder of Jews. Most of the killing took place at six camps in Poland. Hitler called this his **"final solution** to the Jewish question."

The Holocaust

The persecution and mass murder of European Jews during World War II became known as the **Holocaust**. The word *holocaust* means total destruction. The Nazis killed six million Jews—and five million non-Jews, including many Polish, Romani (Gypsies), and Russians. More than one half of European Jews perished in the Holocaust.

Name _____   Date _____

PRACTICE

CALIFORNIA CONTENT STANDARD 10.8.5   *The Holocaust*

Directions: Choose the letter of the *best* answer.

1 Nazi ideology was based on ideas about

  A free enterprise.

  B racial inequality.

  C religious superiority.

  D working-class revolution.

2 The term *Lebensraum* translates roughly as

  A "living space."

  B "final solution."

  C "total destruction."

  D "pure blood."

3 The Nuremberg Laws can be seen as a step toward the Holocaust because they

  A gave Hitler absolute power.

  B resulted in the building of labor camps.

  C deprived Jews of citizenship.

  D described the Nazi policy of genocide.

4 *Kristallnacht* was a defining event in the Holocaust because it was

  A a Nazi death camp.

  B an area where Jews were confined.

  C a set of racial laws.

  D an attack on Jewish homes and businesses.

5 Where were most of the Nazi death camps located?

  A Belgium

  B Germany

  C Poland

  D Russia

6 In April 1943, Jews in the Warsaw ghetto, in Poland, resisted the Nazi army for more than a month, which

  A proved the ineffectiveness of the Nuremberg Laws.

  B stood out as a unique uprising of confined and impoverished people.

  C showed that labor-camp inmates could defeat their oppressors.

  D meant that the Nazis were unable to establish complete control in Poland.

Name _____ Date _____

The Human Costs
of World War II

Specific Objective: Discuss the human costs of war, with particular attention
to the civilian and military losses in Russia, Germany, Britain, the United States,
China, and Japan.

Read the summary to answer questions on the next page.

World War I was once considered so shattering that it was called "the war to end all
wars." But less than 30 years later, the death toll of World War II made it the most
destructive war in history.

| World War II Military Deaths ||
Nation	Estimated Military Losses
Russia	7,000,000
Germany	3,500,000
China	2,200,000
Japan	1,300,000
Britain	350,000
United States	300,000

Civilian Losses

A civilian is a person who is not on active military duty. The total number of civilian
losses during the war may have exceeded the nearly 20 million total military losses.

- Millions of civilians were killed in the Nazi mass exterminations of Jews, Poles, and
  other persecuted groups.

- The civilian death toll was a reason for postwar trials for **war crimes**—acts that
  violate the customs of war, including civilian murder and other crimes against
  humanity. The most famous were the **Nuremberg trials** of Nazi war criminals.

Wounded

In addition to military and civilian deaths, there were more than 13 million military
wounded and more than 6 million civilian wounded.

- The death toll might have been twice as great were it not for **penicillin** and other
  medical advances in treating the wounded.

Total losses—from military and civilian deaths during the war, as well as death from
starvation and disease following the war—have been estimated as high as 40 million.

PRACTICE

CALIFORNIA CONTENT
STANDARD 10.8.6

The Human Costs of World War II

Directions: Choose the letter of the *best* answer.

Use the chart to answer questions 1 and 2.

People Killed by the Nazis*	
Jews	6,000,000
Romani (Gypsies)	400,000
Polish Catholics	3,000,000
Ukrainians and Belorussians	1,000,000
Soviet Prisoners of War	3,500,000
Others (included religious and political opponents; the seriously ill; and those whom the Nazis considered socially undesirable)	1,500,000

*Figures are approximate.

1 What was the *second largest* group of civilians killed by the Nazis?

  A Gypsies

  B Polish Catholics

  C Soviet prisoners of war

  D Ukrainians and Belorussians

2 Which group, killed in Nazi genocide, included Germans?

  A Jews

  B Polish Catholics

  C Soviet prisoners of war

  D Ukrainians and Belorussians

3 It is estimated that millions of lives were saved during World War II because of the discovery of

  A aspirin.

  B contagion theory.

  C the polio vaccine.

  D penicillin.

4 Which event or condition would be *most* significant in a war crimes trial?

  A Rebel groups took up arms against the government.

  B An estimated 200,000 people fled into a neighboring country.

  C The government allowed the mass murder of civilians.

  D The government on trial is one of the world's poorest.

Name _____   Date _____

CALIFORNIA CONTENT STANDARD 10.9.1

Power Shifts Following World War II

Specific Objective: Compare the economic and military power shifts caused by the war, including the Yalta Pact, the development of nuclear weapons, Soviet control over Eastern European nations, and the economic recoveries of Germany and Japan.

Read the summary to answer questions on the next page.

At the end of World War II, the world was left with two main powers: the United States and the Soviet Union. Tensions between them helped to shape the postwar world.

Tensions Begin at the Yalta Conference

When: February 1945

Who: The leaders of the United States, Great Britain, and the Soviet Union

What happened: Allied leaders decided to divide Germany into zones of military occupation. This division was supposed to be temporary.

- The United States wanted a reunited Germany as part of a democratic and economically stable Europe.

- The Soviet Union wanted a divided Germany that lacked power to start wars. An Iron Curtain Falls After the war, not only Germany, but Europe itself, became divided into West and East.

- At the war's end, Soviet troops were stationed in many Eastern European nations. The Soviet Union refused to permit free elections in these nations.

- Soviet authorities took over most of Eastern Europe, isolating it from the west. This isolation was so strong that it was called an **"iron curtain."**

- Eastern Europe became unified with the Soviet Union.

- The nations of Western Europe became unified in opposition to Soviet aggression- Nuclear Weapons Tensions were heightened by nuclear weapons development in the two superpowers.

- **1952** The United States tests the world's first nuclear bomb.

- **1953** The Soviet Union tests its first nuclear bomb. Economic Recovery The economic recoveries of Germany and Japan heralded another power shift.

- In the 1950s, West Germany began an economic boom as an international industrial power with investments in Asia and Africa. (East Germany suffered economically; the Soviets collected war payments from East Germany until 1954.)

- Japan's astonishing economic recovery also began in the 1950s. Japan soon became the world's second-largest economy after the United States.

PRACTICE

CALIFORNIA CONTENT
STANDARD 10.9.1

Power Shifts Following World War II

Directions: Choose the letter of the *best* answer.

1 At the Yalta Conference, the decision was made to

   A divide Germany into occupation zones.

   B begin testing nuclear weapons.

   C form an alliance to defeat Hitler.

   D establish the League of Nations.

2 How was the Soviet Union able to begin taking control of Eastern Europe following World War II?

   A Eastern Europe asked the Soviet Union for economic aid.

   B The Soviet Union offered jobs to impoverished Eastern Europeans.

   C Soviet troops were already stationed in Eastern Europe during the war.

   D Because U.S. President Roosevelt died before the war ended, old treaties were void.

3 After World War II, Western Europe became united in its opposition to

   A nuclear weapons development.

   B investment in foreign markets.

   C a military alliance with the United States.

   D the Soviet Union.

4 After World War II, why did the Soviet Union favor a divided Germany?

   A West Germany lay outside the iron curtain.

   B The Soviet Union wanted exclusive access to East Germany's natural resources.

   C The Soviet Union believed a divided Germany could not start another war.

   D The Soviet Union did not want to be burdened with West Germany's economic problems.

5 Who conducted the world's *first* successful test of a nuclear bomb?

   A Germany

   B Great Britain

   C the Soviet Union

   D the United States

6 Which nation emerged as *one* economic superpower after World War II?

   A Austria

   B Great Britain

   C Japan

   D Korea

Name _____ Date _____

CALIFORNIA CONTENT STANDARD 10.9.2   *The Cold War*

Specific Objective: Analyze the causes of the Cold War, with the free world on one side and Soviet client states on the other, including competition for influence in such places as Egypt, the Congo, Vietnam, and Chile.

Read the summary to answer questions on the next page.

For nearly 45 years (about 1945 to 1991), the United States and the Soviet Union were engaged in hostility that consumed resources and affected world politics as surely as any war. The period became known as the **Cold War**.

The United States	Both	The Soviet Union
• was committed to democratic and capitalist systems • believed the Soviet Union wanted to spread communism to other countries	• wanted to be the dominant power in the world	• was committed to communist political and economic systems • believed the U.S. wanted to suppress revolution in other countries

During the **Cold War**, the Soviet Union and the United States competed for dominance—especially in newly independent Asian and African nations:

- **1960 Congo** Patrice Lumumba, prime minister of the newly independent nation, receives support from the Soviet Union.

- **1954–1979 Egypt** Prime Minister Gamal Abdel Nasser receives support from the Soviet Union.

- **1964–1973 Vietnam** In what begins as a civil war, the United States supports the anti-communist regime of South Vietnam.

- **1973 Chile** The United States supports a bloody overthrow of the socialist government of president Salvador Allende.

As the Cold War became global, many feared the possibility of a third world war, or a full scale nuclear war. The "hottest" or most direct confrontation came during the **Cuban Missile Crisis of 1962**. The U.S. response in the Cuban Missile Crisis was an example of **brinkmanship**—the willingness to go to the brink, or edge, of war in order to force an end to a crisis.

- The United States discovered Soviet missile sites on the island of Cuba.

- The United States blockaded Cuba and threatened to attack the Soviet Union.

- The Soviet Union agreed to remove the missiles.

Name _____ Date _____

PRACTICE

CALIFORNIA CONTENT STANDARD 10.9.2

The Cold War

Directions: Choose the letter of the *best* answer.

Use the quotation to answer questions 1 and 2.

"It shall be the policy of this Nation to regard any nuclear missile launched from Cuba against any nation in the Western Hemisphere as an attack by the Soviet Union on the United States, requiring a full retaliatory response upon the Soviet Union."

—U.S. president John Kennedy, Address on The Cuban Crisis—October 22, 1962

1 According to President Kennedy, the United States would consider "any nuclear missile launched from Cuba" evidence of

A Soviet aggression.

B Cuban nuclear proliferation.

C the globalization of the Cold War.

D an attack on the Western Hemisphere.

2 What policy is reflected in President Kennedy's phrase "a full retaliatory response"?

A brinkmanship

B containment

C isolationism

D nonproliferation

3 How did the Cold War get its name?

A It started in the Soviet Union, which is very cold.

B It took place between the superpowers of the Northern Hemisphere.

C During the war, U.S. and Soviet troops never fought each other directly.

D After 45 years, tensions between the United States and the Soviet Union grew cold.

4 Which is a result of the Cold War?

A The Soviet Union built forced labor camps in Siberia.

B The United States became involved in the Vietnam War.

C The United States was committed to democracy and capitalism.

D The Soviet Union wanted to be the dominant power in the world.

5 Why would the Soviet Union have been *most* interested in providing aid to the Congo in 1960?

A It had valuable natural resources.

B It was a newly independent nation.

C It is located in the center of the African continent.

D It is among the most populous African nations.

Name _____ Date _____

REVIEW

CALIFORNIA CONTENT
STANDARD 10.9.3

*The Truman Doctrine
and the Marshall Plan*

Specific Objective: Understand the importance of the Truman Doctrine and the Marshall Plan, which established the pattern for America's postwar policy of supplying economic and military aid to prevent the spread of Communism and the resulting economic and political competition in arenas such as Southeast Asia (i.e., the Korean War, Vietnam War), Cuba, and Africa.

Read the summary to answer questions on the next page.

Before World War II, the United States mostly followed a policy of **isolationism**—avoiding political or economic ties to other countries. But the Cold War brought a new U.S. foreign policy known as **containment**—acting to contain the spread of communism.

- Under the **Truman Doctrine** (1947), a policy named for then president Harry Truman, the United States offered foreign aid to any country threatened by communist expansion.

- The **Marshall Plan** (1948) provided foreign aid to 16 democratic European nations that struggled to recover from World War II. The United States believed that recovery would help these nations avoid communist influence.

The Truman Doctrine and the Marshall Plan were proof that the United States considered communism a grave threat. They became a foundation of U.S. foreign policy.

1946–1949 **Chinese Civil War** U.S. economic aid helps nationalists fight communists.

1950–1953 **Korean War** U.S. troops help South Korea fight communist North Korea.

1957–1973 **Vietnam War** U.S. troops and economic aid help South Vietnam fight communist North Vietnam.

The United States also supported a number of non-communist leaders in Latin America and Africa—even if those leaders were cruel and unjust, such as the following dictators:

1952–1959 **Cuba,** Fulgencio Batista

1965–1991 **Zaire (Democratic Republic of the Congo),** Mobutu Sese Seko

1973–1990 **Chile,** Augusto Pinochet

PRACTICE

CALIFORNIA CONTENT
STANDARD 10.9.3

The Truman Doctrine and the Marshall Plan

Directions: Choose the letter of the *best* answer.

1 **The Truman Doctrine and the Marshall Plan developed in response to**

   A   the Cold War.

   B   World War II.

   C   a worldwide economic depression.

   D   the McCarthy era.

2 **Under the Truman Doctrine, the United States offered aid to any country that was**

   A   devastated by World War II.

   B   a member of NATO.

   C   a member of the United Nations.

   D   threatened by communist expansion.

3 **The Truman Doctrine is a part of what policy?**

   A   brinksmanship

   B   containment

   C   détente

   D   isolationism

4 **Which statement *best* expresses the relationship between the Truman Doctrine and the Marshall Plan?**

   A   The Truman Doctrine was developed to implement the Marshall Plan.

   B   The Truman Doctrine was developed to limit the Marshall Plan.

   C   The Marshall Plan was an example of the Truman Doctrine.

   D   The Marshall Plan influenced the development of the Truman Doctrine.

5 **Which statement about the Marshall Plan reflects bias or personal opinion?**

   A   It was named for U.S. Secretary of State George Marshall.

   B   It blocked the spread of communism in postwar Europe.

   C   It distributed about $12.5 billion in aid from 1948 to 1951.

   D   It provided more aid to Great Britain than to any other nation.

6 **Why did the United States support Chilean president Augusto Pinochet?**

   A   He was not a communist.

   B   He was a leader in the fight against communism.

   C   He was Chile's first democratically elected leader.

   D   He brought social justice to a formerly communist country.

Name _____   Date _____

Transformation in China

Specific Objective: Analyze the Chinese Civil War, the rise of Mao Tse-Tung, and the subsequent political and economic upheavals in China (e.g., the Great Leap Forward, the Cultural Revolution, and the Tiananmen Square uprising).

Read the summary to answer questions on the next page.

The People's Republic of China

Between 1946 and 1949, civil war raged in China between Nationalist and Communist forces. In October 1949, the Communists were victorious. Their leader, Mao Tse-Tung, renamed the country The People's Republic of China. The communists promised a number of changes:

- Price controls to prevent inflation
- Redistribution of land from owners to workers
- Large-scale industrial development
- A simplified system of Chinese writing, to increase literacy

It was the first time in decades that China was free of Japanese domination. Some of these changes improved life for many in China. But others were disastrous.

The Great Leap Forward

One of Mao's most ambitious programs was the **Great Leap Forward** (1958), which created group farms known as **communes**. At each commune, thousands of people farmed together and lived together in dormitories.

Mao envisioned the Great Leap Forward as a new economic model—China's alternative to the industrial emphasis of Russian communism. Instead, poor planning and severe droughts brought widespread starvation. The program ended in 1960.

The Cultural Revolution

In 1966, Mao launched the **Cultural Revolution** (1966)—a campaign to create an equal society of peasants and workers by purging China of intellectuals, capitalists, and other alleged "counterrevolutionaries." The purge was carried out by militia units of young people, mostly teenagers, known as **Red Guards**.

Chaos followed. The Red Guards imprisoned, tortured, and executed civilians—and destroyed art, antiquities, and other materials of China's heritage. The campaign ended around the time of Mao's death in 1976.

Tiananmen Square

Tiananmen Square, a public plaza in the city of Beijing, has been the site of many political events—but none as well known as the protests of 1989. Students began the protests for **democratic reform**, and in the six weeks that followed were joined by more than a million Chinese from every walk of life. The government crackdown was brutal. Tanks and troops entered Beijing to suppress the protest, killing and injuring thousands of protesters.

PRACTICE

CALIFORNIA CONTENT
STANDARD 10.9.4

Transformation in China

Directions: Choose the letter of the *best* answer.

"The most important problem does not lie in understanding the laws of the objective world and thus being able to explain it, but in applying the knowledge of these laws actively to change the world."

—from *Selected Works, Vol I,* Mao Tse-Tung.

1 The quotation reflects Mao Tse-Tung's commitment to

   A communism.

   B education.

   C science.

   D revolutionary action.

2 What was Chairman Mao's *main* goal for communist China?

   A economic independence and stability

   B a permanent end to civil war

   C preservation of agricultural tradition

   D unity with other Asian countries

3 The Great Leap Forward indicated China's desire to

   A build a People's Army.

   B end Western investment.

   C modernize agriculture.

   D struggle against imperialism.

4 In the late 1950s, in China, a *main* part of the Great Leap Forward program was

   A identifying people according to social class.

   B establishing communes, or collective farms.

   C relocating many rural schools to cities.

   D funding and encouraging political think tanks.

5 Which group was a *main* target of persecution during China's Cultural Revolution?

   A intellectuals

   B peasants

   C party leaders

   D foreign capitalists

6 The Chinese government's response to the 1989 Tiananmen Square protests showed that

   A they opposed democratic reforms.

   B they recognized the will of the people.

   C China was beginning to cooperate with the West.

   D communist leaders were losing their hold on power.

Name _____   Date _____

Resistance in Eastern Europe

Specific Objective: Describe the uprisings in Poland (1952), Hungary (1956), and Czechoslovakia (1968) and those countries' resurgence in the 1970s and 1980s as people in Soviet satellites sought freedom from Soviet control.

Read the summary and graphic organizer to answer questions on the next page.

After World War II, the Soviet Union dominated most of Eastern Europe politically and economically. However, many nations resisted—and ultimately freed themselves from—communist control. Among the first were Poland, Hungary, and Czechoslovakia.

RESISTANCE TO COMMUNIST CONTROL		
HUNGARY 1956 An anti-communist revolt breaks out and Hungarian soldiers and civilians install a new government led by former communist leader **Imre Nagy**. Soviet troops crush the uprising and execute Nagy.	**CZECHOSLOVAKIA 1968** Czech communist leader **Alexander Dubček** begins democratic reforms known as the **Prague Spring**. The Soviet Union invades Czechoslovakia, repeals **Dubček's** reforms, and expels him from the party.	**POLAND 1980** The Polish trade union **Solidarity** launches a strike at a shipyard in Gdansk that becomes world-famous, along with its leader, **Lech Walesa**. By the following year, Solidarity has nearly 10 million members. In 1981, the government bans the union and jails its leaders.

SOVIET UNION 1985 Mikhail Gorbachev takes power amid economic troubles and announces the policies of **glasnost** (openness of information and ideas) and **perestroika** (economic restructuring).

THE COLLAPSE OF COMMUNIST RULE		
HUNGARY 1989 The communist party congress votes to dissolve itself and to pass legislation that will allow for free elections and a democratic political system.	**CZECHOSLOVAKIA 1989** Peaceful student protests launch the **Velvet Revolution**, a mostly nonviolent transition from communist power, as the communist government resigns and is replaced by a non-communist government.	**POLAND 1989** After years of Solidarity launching boycotts and strikes from underground, the government agrees to legalize the union and allow it to participate in elections; Poles vote the communists out of office in favor of Solidarity candidates.

PRACTICE

CALIFORNIA CONTENT
STANDARD 10.9.5

Resistance in Eastern Europe

Directions: Choose the letter of the *best* answer.

1 **What was the outcome of the 1956 uprising in Hungary?**

   A The Soviet Union allowed limited democratic reforms.

   B Soviet troops crushed the uprising and expelled its leader from the party.

   C The Soviet Union allowed limited economic reforms.

   D Soviet troops crushed the uprising and executed its leader.

2 **Who led the months of democratic reform in 1968 that became known as the Prague Spring?**

   A Leonid Brezhnev

   B Alexander Dubček

   C Imre Nagy

   D Lech Walesa

3 **In what country was a successful anticommunist movement led by the trade union Solidarity?**

   A Czechoslovakia

   B Hungary

   C Poland

   D Romania

4 **The fall of the communist governments in Czechoslovakia, Hungary, and Poland occurred four years after the**

   A end of the Cold War.

   B election of Mikhail Gorbachev.

   C Velvet Revolution.

   D Soviet Union began the process of destalinization.

5 **In which nation did the communist party vote to dissolve itself?**

   A Czechoslovakia

   B Hungary

   C Poland

   D Romania

6 **How did the Velvet Revolution earn its name?**

   A It was peaceful.

   B Its effects were superficial.

   C It was led by the wealthy.

   D It was conducted in secret.

Name _____ Date _____

The Creation of the Israeli State

Specific Objective: Understand how the forces of nationalism developed in the Middle East, how the Holocaust affected world opinion regarding the need for a Jewish state, and the significance and effects of the location and establishment of Israel on world affairs.

Read the summary to answer questions on the next page.

Zionism

The political movement known as **Zionism** developed in the late 19th century. Zionists sought to unite Jews around the world and settle them in a new Jewish nation-state. Zionists sought . . .

- to bring together Jews, who were scattered around the world
- a nation-state where Jews could live free from persecution

Most Zionists believed the new state should be created in Palestine the original homeland of the Jews, before the Diaspora—or scattered migrations—began, during the ancient Roman Empire. By the turn of the twentieth century, communities of Zionists in Palestine were working to create a Jewish homeland. Palestine was then a British mandate. In the **Balfour Declaration** (1917), the British promised to support the Zionists, but could not work out a plan to create a Jewish state within Palestine. Great Britain suggested **partitioning** Palestine (dividing it into parts).

The State of Israel

The World War II Holocaust, which resulted in the deaths of six million Jews, created broader international support for Zionism. In 1947, the United Nations called for the partition of Palestine into a Jewish state and a Palestinian state, effective the next year.

Israel on the World Stage

Israel is surrounded by Muslim countries—all of which opposed its creation. It has been in a state of near-constant war with its neighbors since the day it became a nation. Israeli-Palestinian conflict has caused increasing violence in recent years.

The United States and Western Europe remain Israel's main supporters. Israel has also been of strategic interest because it was generally considered the Middle East's only democratic nation—and thus an ally of the West. Meanwhile, much of the Middle East has experienced growing unrest between secular governments and Islamic traditions.

Name _____   Date _____

The Creation of the Israeli State

Directions: Choose the letter of the *best* answer.

Use the map to answer questions 1–4.

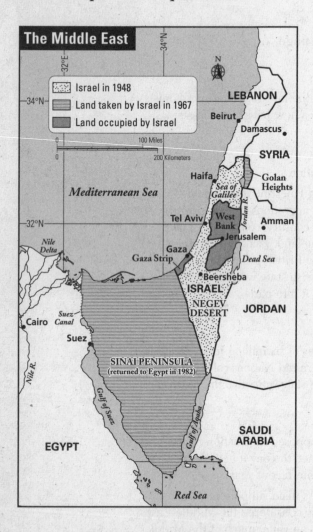

The Middle East

- ⠿ Israel in 1948
- ▤ Land taken by Israel in 1967
- ▨ Land occupied by Israel

0 ___ 100 Miles
0 ___ 200 Kilometers

LEBANON
Beirut
Damascus
SYRIA
Haifa
Sea of Galilee
Golan Heights
Mediterranean Sea
Tel Aviv
West Bank
Amman
Jerusalem
Gaza
Gaza Strip
Dead Sea
Nile Delta
Beersheba
ISRAEL
NEGEV DESERT
JORDAN
Cairo
Suez Canal
Suez
Nile R.
SINAI PENINSULA
(returned to Egypt in 1982)
Gulf of Suez
Gulf of Aqaba
SAUDI ARABIA
EGYPT
Red Sea

1 Israel possessed land bordering the Suez Canal in

A   1955.

B   1965.

C   1975.

D   1985.

2 The acquisition of the Golan Heights caused the *greatest* conflict between Israel and

A   Egypt.

B   Lebanon.

C   Saudi Arabia.

D   Syria.

3 The West Bank is separated from the Mediterranean Sea by

A   the Dead Sea.

B   Israel.

C   Jordan.

D   Lebanon.

4 About how wide is Israel at its widest point?

A   10 miles

B   70 miles

C   140 miles

D   250 miles

5 The state of Israel was created by

A   Great Britain.

B   Palestine.

C   The United Nations.

D   the Balfour Declaration.

Name _____   Date _____

The Collapse of the Soviet Union

Specific Objective: Analyze the reasons for the collapse of the Soviet Union, including the weakness of the command economy, burdens of military commitments, and growing resistance to Soviet rule by dissidents in satellite states and non-Russian Soviet republics.

Read the graphic organizer to answer questions on the next page.

1960s and 1970s: Stagnation of Soviet Life		
Economic problems caused by total government control of the economy	Burdensome cost of arms race and control of communist states	Growing resistance in communist states to tight Soviet control

1980s: Loosening of Soviet Controls		
Policy of **perestroika**— economic restructuring that permitted more local input • local managers make more decisions • small businesses are permitted to open	Changes in foreign policy • efforts to limit arms race • gradual democratization of communist states	Policy of **glasnost**— openness of ideas • greater freedom of the press • release of political prisoners

1991: The Soviet Union Breaks into 11 Republics

PRACTICE

CALIFORNIA CONTENT
STANDARD 10.9.7

The Collapse of the Soviet Union

Directions: Choose the letter of the *best* answer.

1 By the 1970s, the Soviet Union had been significantly weakened by

A   a centrally controlled economy.

B   attacks from abroad.

C   heavy investment in Eastern Europe.

D   German reunification.

2 In the 1980s, Soviet authorities responded to growing resistance to their rule by

A   focusing exclusively on economic development.

B   asserting their military superiority.

C   beginning a gradual process of democratization.

D   jailing political dissidents.

3 Which event in the Soviet Union during the late 1980s is an example of *perestroika*?

A   Gorbachev signed the Intermediate-Range Nuclear Forces Treaty.

B   Local farmers were allowed to set their own prices.

C   Soviet troops were withdrawn from Afghanistan.

D   Churches were permitted to re-open.

4 Which event in the Soviet Union during the late 1980s is an example of *glasnost*?

A   Small businesses were permitted to open.

B   Gorbachev limited arms spending.

C   The Chernobyl nuclear power plant exploded.

D   Previously banned books were published.

5 A *main* reason the Soviet Union decided in the 1980s to pursue arms control was that the arms race had

A   caused fear among Soviet citizens.

B   strained relations with Europe.

C   burdened the Soviet economy.

D   made the Soviet Union dependent on foreign materials.

6 The breakup of the Soviet Union, in 1991, can *best* be characterized as

A   a relatively peaceful transition.

B   a complete economic disaster.

C   an example of international cooperation.

D   an effort that lasted nearly a century.

Name _____ Date _____

CALIFORNIA CONTENT STANDARD 10.9.8

International Cooperation After World War II

Specific Objective: Discuss the establishment and work of the United Nations and the purposes and functions of the Warsaw Pact, SEATO, NATO, and the Organization of American States.

Read the summary to answer questions on the next page.

After World War II, several organizations were established to promote international cooperation and security. The largest and most influential was the United Nations.

The United Nations (founded 1945)

Members: At its founding, 51 members; now a global organization of 191 members

Purposes

- promote world peace and security
- develop friendly relations among nations
- cooperate in solving international problems

Structure: The United Nations has three major organizations

- The **Secretariat**, the administrative center, headed by the **Secretary-General**
- The **Security Council**, the main peacekeeping body, with 15 members
- The **General Assembly**, a forum for all members to discuss world issues

In addition, several alliances formed to promote security and cooperation among their member nations. Cold War tensions were a factor in the development of each.

Alliance (Year Founded)	Founding Members	Purpose(s)	Recent History
Organization of American States (OAS) (1948)	20 Central and South American nations plus the United States	promote peace, economic development, territorial integrity, and democracy in the region	now has 35 member nations (Cuba is excluded from participation); 47 additional nations and the European Union are "permanent observers"
North Atlantic Treaty Organization (NATO) (1949)	10 Western European nations plus the United States and Canada	provide mutual defense; formed out of Cold War concerns about Soviet aggression	now has 26 members; focuses on stability in Europe and peacekeeping in Europe and beyond
The Warsaw Pact (1955)	7 Eastern European nations plus the Soviet Union	provide mutual defense; Soviet bloc alliance in response to NATO	dissolved in 1991 following the collapse of the Soviet Union
Southeast Asia Treaty Organization (SEATO) (1955)	Australia, France, Great Britain, New Zealand, Pakistan, the Philippines, Thailand, and the U.S.	prevent the spread of communism in Southeast Asia	dissolved in 1977 following internal conflicts about Vietnam War

Name _____   Date _____

PRACTICE

International Cooperation After World War II

Directions: Choose the letter of the *best* answer.

1 The development of the United Nations arose from concerns about

   A economic recovery following World War II.

   B global security during the Cold War.

   C world peace following World War II.

   D Soviet aggression during the Cold War.

2 The organization of the United Nations that provides a forum for all member nations is the

   A General Assembly.

   B Secretariat.

   C Secretary-General.

   D Security Council.

3 What alliance was established by nations who feared Soviet aggression?

   A NATO

   B OAS

   C SEATO

   D The Warsaw Pact

4 Which alliance would have proclaimed in its charter that "the historic mission of America is to offer to man a land of liberty"?

   A NATO

   B OAS

   C SEATO

   D The Warsaw Pact

5 The establishment of the Warsaw Pact was associated with

   A World War I.

   B World War II.

   C the Cold War.

   D the Vietnam War.

6 SEATO was founded by representatives from

   A Asia.

   B anticommunist nations.

   C communist nations.

   D various nations, both communist and anticommunist

Name _____ Date _____

Challenges in Modern Nation Building (Case Studies)

Specific Objective: Analyze nation-building (in at least two of: the Middle East, Africa, Mexico, Central and South America, and China). Understand the challenges faced. Include geopolitical, cultural, military, and economic issues and international relationships.

Read the case histories to answer questions on the next page.

Modern Nation Building Case Study: China

Key Challenge Balance liberalized economic system with authoritarian political system

Economic Issues

- Beginning in the late 1970s, China began a series of **economic reforms** under the leadership of **Deng Xiaoping**. His **Four Modernizations** brought some private ownership and growth to agriculture, industry, the military, and science.

- The liberalized economy boomed in the 1990s. Life for many Chinese improved. But many people—especially the half living in rural areas—remained in poverty.

Cultural / Geopolitical / Military Issues

- As technology, foreign investment, tourism, and Western popular culture increased in China, so did demands for individual rights and democracy.

- Protests and strikes against the government in the 1980s peaked in 1989, when a student-led protest in Beijing's **Tiananmen Square** led to a military crackdown.

- Deng Xiaoping and subsequent leaders worked to improve international relations. But diplomatic tensions exist because China remains a one-party state that represses both individual rights and outspoken discussion of democracy.

Modern Nation Building Case Study: Mexico

Key Challenge Improve economic problems and continue democratic advances.

Economic Issues

- Mexico experienced economic growth in the last half of the 20th century, but most of the benefits went to a wealthy minority.

- Over half of Mexicans live in poverty, with a low **standard of living** (economic success, as measured by the amount of goods available to the average citizen).

- In the 1990s, following a drop in world oil prices, Mexico, a leading oil producer, experienced a **recession**—an economic slowdown.

- In the early 2000s, a downturn in the U.S. economy eliminated hundreds of thousands of jobs in Mexico, which has close economic ties to the United States.

Cultural / Geopolitical / Military Issues

- Among those living in poverty in Mexico are many with ancestral native roots.

- In 1994, an uprising of revolutionaries called **Zapatistas** in the state of Chiapas called for reforms to aid indigenous (ancestral native) people, especially the **Maya**.

- Mexico is transitioning from single-party rule by the **PRI** (revolutionary party) to a more democratic system. Currently, different parties have a voice in government.

PRACTICE

CALIFORNIA CONTENT
STANDARD 10.10.1

*Challenges in Modern Nation
Building (Case Studies)*

Directions: Choose the letter of the *best* answer.

1 **A nation's standard of living would *most* likely be measured by**

   A the total sum of its exports.

   B its annual rate of inflation.

   C its annual rate of economic growth.

   D the average income per person.

2 **A slowdown in a nation's economy is known as a**

   A deficit.

   B depreciation.

   C devaluation.

   D recession.

3 **The 1989 protests for democracy in Tiananmen Square followed the**

   A death of Deng Xiaoping.

   B admission of China to the World Trade Organization (WTO).

   C first ten years of economic liberalization in China.

   D signing of the UN Universal Declaration of Human Rights.

4 **Deng Xiaoping's Four Modernizations were a set of goals toward improving China's**

   A agricultural productivity.

   B struggling economy.

   C foreign relations.

   D human-rights record.

5 **How did 50 years of economic growth affect income distribution in Mexico?**

   A A middle class has emerged.

   B The gap between rich and poor has grown.

   C All economic classes have benefited

   D Industrial workers have benefited the most.

6 **The Zapatistas who led a 1994 uprising in the Mexican state of Chiapas were a voice for**

   A civilian government.

   B free elections.

   C indigenous peoples.

   D land reform.

REVIEW

CALIFORNIA CONTENT
STANDARD 10.10.2

Recent Regional Histories (Case Studies)

Specific Objective: Describe the recent history of the regions (see 10.10.1, p. 107), including political divisions and systems, key leaders, religious issues, natural features, resources, and population patterns.

Read the case histories to answer questions on the next page.

Case Study: China

Political System communist state

Key Leader President Hu Jintao (came to power 2003)

Economy growing quickly since the early 1990s

Recent Events / Issues

- In 1997, the former British colony of Hong Kong became a part of China, which promised to respect Hong Kong's economic and political laws for 50 years.
- In 2001, due to economic and diplomatic progress, China was admitted to the World Trade Organization (WTO), gaining trading rights of capitalist countries.

Current Events / Issues

- China is the world's most populous country, with 1.3 billion people.
- Migration to cities has increased with the growth of industry and services.
- China is the world's top producer of coal and is a leading producer of other minerals and of industrial exports, such as machinery, clothing, and footwear.
- China has the fastest-growing developing economy in the world; however, there is significant unemployment and poverty in rural areas.
- Industrial pollution has negatively affected the environment and public health.

Case Study: Mexico

Political System federal republic

Key Leader President Vicente Fox Quesada (elected 2000)

Economy depends heavily on oil, tourism, and *maquiladoras*

Recent Events / Issues

- The 1980s brought heavy foreign investment in *maquiladoras*—manufacturing plants that produce goods for export to the United States.
- The boom of *maquiladoras* in the 1980s and 1990s brought a population shift to U.S.–Mexico border areas.
- In 1994, NAFTA (North American Free Trade Agreement) greatly increased trade among Mexico, the U.S., and Canada, by easing import restrictions and fees.
- The 2000 election of President Vicente Fox Quesada ended 71 years of single-party PRI (revolutionary party) rule.

Current Events / Issues:

- Petroleum is Mexico's top natural resource; it used to represent about 75 percent of the nation's exports, but the economy is now more diversified.
- Mexico's natural beauty and history have made tourism an important industry.

PRACTICE

CALIFORNIA CONTENT
STANDARD 10.10.2

Recent Regional Histories (Case Studies)

Directions: Choose the letter of the *best* answer.

1 Changes in the Chinese economy since the 1970s have caused a significant population migration to

A   cities.

B   foreign countries.

C   rural areas.

D   overseas territories.

2 After Hong Kong was returned to Chinese rule, China promised that it would

A   develop Hong Kong's sagging economy.

B   integrate Hong Kong into China's political and economic systems.

C   make Hong Kong into a free port.

D   respect the laws of Hong Kong for 50 years.

3 China's admission to the World Trade Organization (WTO) indicated that it had

A   abandoned communist ideals.

B   entered the global marketplace.

C   improved its human rights record.

D   modernized its banking system.

4 What is the *most likely* reason for a dramatic increase in bilingual Spanish-English labeling on products sold in Canada and the United States?

A   U.S. investment in Mexican banks

B   the North American Free Trade Agreement

C   immigration from the United States to Mexico

D   increased Spanish literacy among English speakers

5 In Mexico, the production plants known as *maquiladoras* produce goods for

A   sale within Mexico.

B   export to the United States.

C   European Union markets.

D   commerce in Central and South America.

Name _____ Date _____

REVIEW

CALIFORNIA CONTENT
STANDARD 10.10.3

Conditions for Democracy (Case Studies)

Specific Objective: Discuss the important trends in the regions (see 10.10.1, p. 107) today and whether they appear to serve the cause of individual freedom and democracy.

Read the summary and the chart to answer questions on the next page.

China and Mexico are both in periods of transition. Recently, both have experienced significant economic growth—and, at times, demands for greater democratic freedoms. The chart shows the practices that are needed to make democracy work, and how conditions in China and Mexico could affect those practices.

Conditions for Democracy: Case Studies		
Democratic Practice	**China**	**Mexico**
Free Elections ***Needed:*** voting rights; more than one political party	• For more than 50 years, only one political party—the Communist party—has been allowed.	• In 2000, Mexico had its first presidential primary, followed by the end of single-party rule.
Citizen Participation ***Needed:*** guaranteed freedom of expression; economic stability; literacy	• The Communist party limits freedom of speech and the press. • The economy is growing. • Literacy has risen to 86% (2003), up from 20% in 1949.	• News media has often been subject to government pressure. The economy is growing. • Literacy has risen to 92% (2003), up from less than 10% in 1917.
Individual Rights ***Needed:*** guarantees of individual rights and equality before the law	• The Communist party does not tolerate dissent. • The party has detained many political prisoners and restricted freedom of speech.	• The constitution of 1917 names various rights, including freedom of religion and the right to receive an education.
Constitutional Government ***Needed:*** a government based on widely understood laws that apply to everyone	• The Chinese constitution of 1982 states that the law is above the Communist party. • The party has significantly revised the constitution four times.	• The constitution of 1917 laid the groundwork for a federal republic with a balance of powers.

Name _____ Date _____

Conditions for Democracy (Case Studies)

Directions: Choose the letter of the *best* answer.

> "The solution to national problems begins with our own determination to confront them. Democracy becomes reality every time one of us takes on the responsibility of changing Mexico."
>
> —from Mexican president Vicente Fox Quesada's State of the Union speech, September 1, 2004

1 **What central practice of democracy is President Fox describing in the quotation?**

A voting rights

B citizen participation

C equality before the law

D constitutional government

2 **What condition is necessary in establishing a democratic nation?**

A economic growth

B free elections

C a presidency

D UN membership

3 **Which fact, relating to the history of China's constitution, suggests that China may not have the current conditions for democracy?**

A It was not adopted until 1982.

B It was recently revised four times by the ruling party.

C It describes citizens' "fundamental rights and duties."

D It forbids the secession (withdrawal) of any territory.

4 **Which fact about the Chinese population is *most* likely to have contributed to recent demands for democratic reform?**

A About half of the people work in agriculture.

B China has the largest population of any nation in the world.

C More than 100 dialects are spoken in China.

D In the last 50 years, literacy increased from about 20% to more than 85%.

5 **How did Mexico's presidential election in 2000 bring the country closer to democracy than previous elections?**

A There was a peaceful exchange of power.

B It overturned a military dictatorship.

C There was no clear winner.

D It brought the end of single-party rule.

6 **One way Mexico's constitution of 1917 helped to lay groundwork for democracy was by**

A including a bill of rights.

B setting term limits for the president.

C proclaiming national ownership of natural resources.

D limiting ownership of property by foreigners and the Church.

Name _____   Date _____

The Rise of a Global Economy

Specific Objective: Analyze the integration of countries into the world economy and analyze the information, technical, and communications revolutions.

Read the graphic organizer to answer questions on the next page.

Technology

- Satellites link telephone, radio, and television networks.
- Computers and the Internet transmit information.
- Television broadcasts news and popular culture.

Trade Agreements

- Free trade (the removal of barriers such as import taxes) builds markets.
- Trade blocs such as the North American Free Trade Association (NAFTA) and the European Union (EU) form agreements to encourage economic cooperation.

Global Economic Growth

Multinational Corporations

- Companies have parts of their business in different countries.
- Product design and marketing takes place in developed (industrialized) nations.
- Manufacturing takes place in developing (industrializing) nations.

Environmental Impact

- Manufacturing requires large amounts of energy and other resources.
- Industrial pollution has damaged the ozone layer and caused global warming.
- Economists and environmentalists are working toward sustainable development—growing the economy while preserving the environment.

Name _____ Date _____

Directions: Choose the letter of the *best* answer.

1 Which force has had the *greatest* effect in increasing contact among people in the world?

A   economic expansion

B   immigration

C   new technology

D   regional trade

2 What is a *main* role of developing nations in the rise of the global economy?

A   Products are designed in developing nations.

B   Products are manufactured in developing nations.

C   Developing nations export products to less industrialized nations.

D   Developing nations share their technology with developed nations.

3 Free trade can stimulate economic growth by

A   increasing access to international transportation.

B   linking regional trade associations.

C   permitting manufacturers to set their own prices.

D   removing barriers such as tariffs.

4 A multinational corporation is defined by the fact that it

A   is publicly owned by shareholders.

B   produces goods for international markets.

C   uses natural resources from other countries.

D   has operations in more than one country.

5 As a result of globalization, both developed and developing nations have

A   become more dependent on other nations.

B   gained access to new technology.

C   reduced damage to the environment.

D   increased manufacturing jobs.

6 The goal of sustainable development is to meet nations' economic needs while ensuring

A   global cooperation.

B   international access to natural resources.

C   preservation of the environment.

D   rights for workers in developed nations.